OLD MOORE'S

HOROSCOPE AND ASTRAL DIARY

CANCER

OLD MOORE'S

HOROSCOPE AND ASTRAL DIARY

CANCER

foulsham
LONDON • NEW YORK • TORONTO • SYDNEY

foulsham

The Old Barrel Store, Drayman's Lane, Marlow, Bucks SL7 2FF

Foulsham books can be found in all good bookshops and direct from
www.foulsham.com

ISBN: 978-0-572-04492-3

A CIP record for this book is available from the British Library

Typeset in Great Britain by Chris Brewer Origination, Christchurch

CONTENTS

INTRODUCTION

Astrology has been a part of life for centuries now, and no matter how technological our lives become, it seems that it never diminishes in popularity. For thousands of years people have been gazing up at the star-clad heavens and seeing their own activities and proclivities reflected in the movement of those little points of light. Across centuries countless hours have been spent studying the way our natures, activities and decisions seem to be paralleled by their predictable movements. Old Moore, a time-served veteran in astrological research, continues to monitor the zodiac and has produced the Astral Diary for 2015, tailor-made to your own astrological makeup.

Old Moore's Astral Diary is unique in its ability to get the heart of your nature and to offer you the sort of advice that might come from a trusted friend. It enables you to see in a day-by-day sense exactly how the planets are working for you. The diary section advises how you can get the best from upcoming situations and allows you to plan ahead successfully. There's also room on each daily entry to record your own observations or appointments.

While other popular astrology books merely deal with your astrological 'Sun sign', the Astral Diaries go much further. Every person on the planet is unique and Old Moore allows you to access your individuality in a number of ways. The front section gives you the chance to work out the placement of the Moon at the time of your birth and to see how its position has set an important seal on your overall nature. Perhaps most important of all, you can use the Astral Diary to discover your Rising Sign. This is the zodiac sign that was appearing over the Eastern horizon at the time of your birth and is just as important to you as an individual as is your Sun sign.

It is the synthesis of many different astrological possibilities that makes you what you are and with the Astral Diaries you can learn so much. How do you react to love and romance? Through the unique Venus tables and the readings that follow them, you can learn where the planet Venus was at the time of your birth. It is even possible to register when little Mercury is 'retrograde', which means that it appears to be moving backwards in space when viewed from the Earth. Mercury rules communication, so be prepared to deal with a few setbacks in this area when you see the sign ☿. The Astral Diary will be an interest and a support throughout the whole year ahead.

Old Moore extends his customary greeting to all people of the Earth and offers his age-old wishes for a happy and prosperous period ahead.

THE ESSENCE
OF CANCER

Exploring the Personality of
Cancer the Crab

(22ND JUNE – 22ND JULY)

What's in a sign?

The most obvious fact about you, particularly when viewed by others, is that you are trustworthy. Sometimes this fact gets on your nerves. Many Cancerians long to be bigger, bolder and more ruthless, but it simply isn't the way you were made. You are basically ruled by your emotions and there is very little you can do to get away from the fact. Once you realise this you could be in for a happy life but there are bound to be some frustrations on the way.

Your ruling planet is the Moon, which changes its position in astrological terms far more quickly than any other heavenly body. That's why you can sometimes feel that you have experienced a whole year's emotions in only a month. However the saving grace of this fact is that unlike the other Water signs of Scorpio and Pisces, you are rarely bogged down by emotional restraints for more than a day or two at a time. This gives you a more optimistic attitude and a determination to use your natural talents to the full, even in the face of some adversity. Caring for others is second nature to you and forms a very large part of your life and character.

Your attitude towards romance fluctuates but is generally of the 'story book' sort. Once you commit yourself to another person, either romantically or practically, you are not likely to change your mind very easily. Loyalty is part of what you are about and doesn't change just because things sometimes get a little complicated. Even when you don't really know where you are going, you are inclined to pull those you love along the path with you, and you can usually rely on their assistance. Basically you are very easy to love and there can't be anything much wrong with that fact. At the same time you can be very practical, don't mind doing some of the dirty work and are in your element when those around you are floundering.

The creative potential within your nature is strong. You are a natural homemaker and tend to get a great deal from simply watching others succeed. All the same this isn't the whole story because you are complex and inclined to be too worrisome.

Cancer resources

Your ruling planet is the Moon, Earth's closest neighbour in space. This means that you are as subject to its tides and fluctuations as is our planet. Of course this is a double-edged sword because you can sometimes be an emotional maelstrom inside. To compensate for this fact you have a level of personal sensitivity that would be admired by many. At the same time you have a deep intuition and can usually be relied upon to see through the mist of everyday life and to work out how situations are likely to mature. This is especially true when it comes to assessing those around you.

As a homemaker you are second to none. You can make a few pounds go a very long way and can cope well in circumstances that would greatly trouble those around you. Adversity is not something that bothers you too much at all and it is clear that you can even revel in difficulty. Nothing is too much trouble when you are dealing with people you really love – which includes friends as well as family members.

One of the greatest Cancerian resources is the ability to bring a practical face to even difficult circumstances. Physically speaking you are very resilient, even if you don't always seem to be the strongest person around in an emotional sense. You are given to showing extreme kindness, sometimes even in the face of cruelty from others, though if you are genuinely provoked you can show an anger that would shock most people, even those who think they know you very well indeed.

What really counts the most is your ability to bring others round to your point of view and to get them to do what you think is best. Working from example you won't generally expect others to do anything you are not prepared to try yourself, and your attitude can be an inspiration to others. Through hard work and perseverance you can build a good life for yourself, though your consideration for those around you never diminishes and so even a fortune gained would generally be used on behalf of the world around you. The greatest resource that you possess is your capacity to love and to nurture. This makes you successful and well loved by others.

Beneath the surface

The most difficult aspect of those born under the sign of Cancer the Crab is trying to work out the psychological motivations of this apparently simple but actually deeply complex zodiac position. 'Emotion' is clearly the keyword and is the fountain from which everything, good and bad alike, flows. Whilst some zodiac sign types are inclined to act and then consider the consequences, the Crab is a different beast altogether. The main quality of Cancer is caring. This applies as much to the world at large as it does in consideration of family, though to the Crab it's clear that under almost all circumstances family comes first.

You are a deep thinker and don't always find it easy to explain the way your mind is working. The reason for this is not so difficult to understand. Feelings are not the same as thoughts and it is sometimes quite difficult to express the qualities that rule you internally. What you seem to prefer to do is to put a caring arm around the world and express your inner compassion in this manner. You might also sometimes be a little anxious that if others knew how your innermost mind worked you would become more vulnerable than you already are – which is why the Crab wears a shell in the first place.

At the first sign of emotional pressure from outside you are inclined to retreat into yourself. As a result you don't always confront issues that would be best dealt with immediately. This proclivity runs deep and strong in your nature and can sometimes cause you much more trouble than would be the case if you just made the right statements and asked the correct questions. Physically and mentally you are not inclined to withdraw because you are very much stronger than the world would give you credit for.

Cancerians have a tremendous capacity to love, allied to a potential for positive action when the lives or well-being of others is threatened. In some ways you are the bravest zodiac sign of all because you will march forward into the very gates of hell if you know that you can be of service to those around you. From family to village or town, from town to nation and from nation to a global awareness, yours is the zodiac sign that best epitomises humanity's struggle for a universal understanding.

Making the best of yourself

If you start out from the premise that you are well liked by most people then you are halfway towards any intended destination. Of course you don't always register your popularity and are given to worrying about the impression you give. The picture you paint of yourself is usually very different from the one the world at large sees. If you doubt this, ask some of your best friends to describe your nature and you will be quite surprised. You need to be as open as possible to avoid internalising matters that would be best brought into a more public arena. Your natural tendency to look after everyone else masks a desire to get on in life personally, and the Cancerians who succeed the best are the ones who have somehow managed to bring a sense of balance to their giving and taking.

Try to avoid being too quiet. In social situations you have much to offer, though would rarely do so in a particularly gregarious manner. Nevertheless, and partly because you don't shoot your mouth off all the time, people are willing to listen to what you have to say. Once you realise how strong your influence can be you are already on the road to riches – financial and personal.

Use your imagination to the full because it is one of the most potent weapons in your personal armoury. People won't underestimate you when they know how strong you really are and that means that life can sometimes be less of a struggle. But under most circumstances be your usual warm self, and the love you desire will come your way.

The very practical issues of life are easy for you to deal with, which is why your material success is generally assured. All that is needed to make the picture complete is more confidence in your ability to lead and less inclination to follow.

The impressions you give

There is no doubt at all that you are one of the most loved and the most admired people around. It isn't hard to see why. Your relatives and friends alike feel very protected and loved, which has got to be a good start when it comes to your contacts with the world at large.

The most intriguing thing about being a Cancerian subject is how different you appear to be when viewed by others as against the way you judge your own personality. This is down to external appearances as much as anything. For starters you usually wear a cheery smile, even on those occasions when it is clear you are not smiling inside. You give yourself fully to the needs and wants of those around you and are very sympathetic, even towards strangers. It's true that you may not fully exploit the implications of your pleasant nature – but that's only another typical part of your character.

Those people who know you the best are aware that you have a great capacity to worry about things, and they may also understand that you are rarely as confident as you give the external impression of being. They sense the deeply emotional quality of your nature and can observe the long periods of deep thought. When it comes to the practicalities of life, however, you perhaps should not be surprised that you are sometimes put on rather too much. Even this is understandable because you rarely say no and will usually make yourself available when there is work to be done.

True success for the Cancer subject lies in recognising your strong points and in being willing to gain from them in a personal sense from time to time. You also need to realise that, to others, the impression you give is what you really are. Bridging the gap between outward calm and inner confusion might be the most important lesson.

The way forward

Although you don't always feel quite as sure of yourself as you give the impression of being, you can still exploit your external appearance to your own and other people's advantage. Your strong sense of commitment to family and your ability to get on well in personal relationships are both factors that improve your ability to progress in life.

Achieving a sense of balance is important. For example you can spend long hours locked into your own thoughts, but this isn't good for you in an exclusive sense. Playing out some of your fantasies in the real world can do you good, even though you are aware that this involves taking chances, something you don't always care to do. At the same time you should not be afraid to make gains as a result of the way you are loved by others. This doesn't come for free and you work long and hard to establish the affection that comes your way.

In practical matters you are capable and well able to get on in life. Money comes your way, not usually as a result of particularly good luck, but because you are a tireless and steady worker. You can accept responsibility, even though the implied management side of things worries you somewhat. To have a career is important because it broadens your outlook and keeps you functioning in the wider world, which is where your personal successes take place. The more you achieve, the greater is the level of confidence that you feel – which in turn leads to even greater progress.

Cancerians should never cut themselves off from the mainstream of life. It's true you have many acquaintances but very few really close friends, but that doesn't matter. Practically everyone you know is pleased to name you as a trusted ally, which has to be the best compliment of all to your apparently serene and settled nature.

In love you are ardent and sincere. It may take you a while to get round to expressing the way you feel, partly because you are a little afraid of failure in this most important area of your life. All the same you love with a passion and are supportive to your partner. Family will always be the most important sphere of life because your zodiac sign rules the astrological fourth house, which is essentially dedicated to home and family matters. If you are contented in this arena it tends to show in other areas of your life too. Your affable nature is your best friend and only tends to disappear if you allow yourself to become too stressed.

CANCER ON THE CUSP

Old Moore is often asked how astrological profiles are altered for those people born at either the beginning or the end of a zodiac sign, or, more properly, on the cusps of a sign. In the case of Cancer this would be on the 22nd of June and for two or three days after, and similarly at the end of the sign, probably from the 20th to the 22nd of July. In this year's Astral Diaries, once again, Old Moore sets out to explain the differences regarding cuspid signs.

The Gemini Cusp – June 22nd to June 24th

You are certainly fun to be around and the sign of Gemini has a great deal to do with your basic motivations. As a result, you tend to be slightly more chatty than the average Cancerian and usually prove to be the life and soul of any party that is going on in your vicinity. Not everyone understands the basic sensitivity that lies below the surface of this rather brash exterior, however, and you can sometimes be a little hurt if people take you absolutely at face value.

There probably isn't the total consistency of emotional responses that one generally expects to find in the Crab when taken alone, and there are times when you might be accused of being rather fickle. All the same, you have a big heart and show genuine concern for anyone in trouble, especially the underdog. Your Gemini attributes give you the opportunity to speak your mind, so when it comes to aiding the world you can be a tireless reformer and show a great ability to think before you speak, which is not typical of Gemini on its own, although there are occasions when the two sides of your nature tend to be at odds with each other.

At work you are very capable and can be relied upon to make instant decisions whenever necessary. Your executive capabilities are pronounced and you are more than capable of thinking on your feet, even if you prefer to mull things over if possible. You are the sort of person that others tend to rely on for advice and will not usually let your colleagues or friends down.

In matters of love, you are less steadfast and loyal than the Crab, yet you care very deeply for your loved ones. People like to have you around and actively seek your advice which, in the main, is considered and sound, though always delivered with humour. You love to travel and would never wish to be limited in either your horizons or your lifestyle. All in all, you are a fun person, good to know, and basically sensible.

The Leo Cusp – July 20th to July 22nd

Here we find a Cancerian who tends to know what he or she wants from life. Part of the natural tendency of the Crab is to be fairly shy and retiring, though progressively less so as the Sun moves on towards the sign of Leo. You are probably aware that you don't exactly match the Cancer stereotype and are likely to be more outspoken, determined and even argumentative at times. You have lofty ideals, which find a ready home for the sensitive qualities that you draw from Cancer. Many social reformers tend to have their Suns very close to the Leo cusp of Cancer and people born on this cusp like to work hard for the world, especially for the less well-off members of society.

In matters of love, you are deep, but ardent and sincere, finding better ways of expressing your emotions verbally than those generally associated with the Crab. You are capable at work, easily able to take on responsibilities that involve controlling other people, and you are outwardly braver than often seems to be the case with Cancer alone. Not everyone finds you particularly easy to understand, probably because there are some definite paradoxes about your nature.

A few problems come along in the area of ideals, which are more important to you than they would be to some of the people with whom you associate. You need to be sure of yourself, a fact that leads to fairly long thinking periods, but once you have formed a particular belief you will move heaven and earth to demonstrate how sensible it is. Don't be too alarmed if not everyone agrees with you.

You are not the typical conformist that might more usually be the case with Cancerians, and feel the need to exercise your civic rights to the full. Tireless when dealing with something you think is especially important, you are a good and loyal friend, a staunch and steadfast lover and you care deeply about your family. However, you are not as confrontational as a person born completely under Leo, and therefore can usually be relied upon to seek a compromise.

CANCER AND ITS ASCENDANTS

The nature of every individual on the planet is composed of the rich variety of zodiac signs and planetary positions that were present at the time of their birth. Your Sun sign, which in your case is Cancer, is one of the many factors when it comes to assessing the unique person you are. Probably the most important consideration, other than your Sun sign, is to establish the zodiac sign that was rising over the eastern horizon at the time that you were born. This is your Ascending or Rising sign. Most popular astrology fails to take account of the Ascendant, and yet its importance remains with you from the very moment of your birth, through every day of your life. The Ascendant is evident in the way you approach the world, and so, when meeting a person for the first time, it is this astrological influence that you are most likely to notice first. Our Ascending sign essentially represents what we appear to be, while the Sun sign is what we feel inside ourselves.

The Ascendant also has the potential for modifying our overall nature. For example, if you were born at a time of day when Cancer was passing over the eastern horizon (this would be around the time of dawn) then you would be classed as a double Cancerian. As such, you would typify this zodiac sign, both internally and in your dealings with others. However, if your Ascendant sign turned out to be a Fire sign, such as Aries, there would be a profound alteration of nature, away from the expected qualities of Cancer.

One of the reasons why popular astrology often ignores the Ascendant is that it has always been rather difficult to establish. Old Moore has found a way to make this possible by devising an easy-to-use table, which you will find on page 125 of this book. Using this, you can establish your Ascendant sign at a glance. You will need to know your rough time of birth, then it is simply a case of following the instructions.

For those readers who have no idea of their time of birth it might be worth allowing a good friend, or perhaps your partner, to read through the section that follows this introduction. Someone who deals with you on a regular basis may easily discover your Ascending sign, even though you could have some difficulty establishing it for yourself. A good understanding of this component of your nature is essential if you want to be aware of that 'other person' who is responsible for the way you make contact with the world at large. Your Sun sign, Ascendant sign, and the other pointers in this book will, together, allow you a far better understanding of what makes you tick as an individual. Peeling back the different layers of your astrological make-up can be an enlightening experience, and the Ascendant may represent one of the most important layers of all.

Cancer with Cancer Ascendant

You are one of the most warm and loving individuals that it is possible to know, and you carry a quiet dignity that few would fail to recognise. Getting on with things in your own steady way, you are, nevertheless, capable of great things, simply because you keep going. Even in the face of adversity your steady but relentless pace can be observed, and much of what you do is undertaken on behalf of those you love the most. On the other side of the coin you represent something of a mystery and it is also true that emotionally speaking you tend to be very highly charged. It doesn't take much to bring you to tears and you are inclined to have a special affection for the underdog, which on occasions can get you into a little trouble. Although it is your natural way to keep a low profile, you will speak out loudly if you think that anyone you care for is under attack, and yet you don't show the same tendency on your own behalf.

Rarely if ever out of control, you are the levelling influence everyone feels they need in their life, which is one of the reasons why you are so loved. Your quiet ways are accepted by the world, which is why some people will be astonished when you suddenly announce that you are about to travel overland to Asia. What a great puzzle you can be, but that is half the attraction.

Cancer with Leo Ascendant

This can be a very fortunate combination, for when seen at its best it brings all the concern and the natural caring qualities of Cancer, allied to the more dynamic and very brave face of Leo. Somehow there is a great deal of visible energy here, but it manifests itself in a way that always shows a concern for the world at large. No matter what charitable works are going on in your district it is likely that you will be involved in one way or another, and you relish the cut and thrust of life much more than the the retiring side of Cancer would seem to do. You are quite capable of walking alone and don't really need the company of others for large chunks of the average day. However, when you are in social situations you fare very well and can usually be observed with a smile on your face.

Conversationally speaking you have sound, considered opinions and often represent the voice of steady wisdom when faced with a situation that means arbitration. In fact you will often be put in this situation, and there is more than one politician and union representative who shares this undeniably powerful zodiac combination. Like all those associated with the sign of Cancer you love to travel and can make a meal out of your journeys with brave, intrepid Leo lending a hand in both the planning and the doing

Cancer with Virgo Ascendant

What can this union of zodiac signs bring to the party that isn't there in either Cancer or Virgo alone? Well, quite a bit actually. Virgo can be very fussy on occasions and too careful for its own good. The presence of steady, serene Cancer alters the perspectives and allows a smoother, more flowing individual to greet the world. You are chatty and easy to know, and exhibit a combination of the practical skills of Virgo, together with the deep and penetrating insights that are typical of Cancer. This can make you appear to be very powerful and your insights are second to none. You are a born organiser and love to be where things are happening, even if you are only there to help make the sandwiches or to pour the tea. Invariably your role will be much greater but you don't seek personal acclaim and are a good team player on most occasions.

There is a quiet side to your nature and those who live with you will eventually get used to your need for solitude. This seems strange because Virgo is generally such a chatterbox and, taken on its own, is rarely quiet for long. In matters of love you show great affection and a sense of responsibility that makes you an ideal parent. It is sometimes the case, however, that you care rather more than you should be willing to show.

Cancer with Libra Ascendant

What an absolutely pleasant and approachable sort of person you are, and how much you have to offer. Like most people associated with the sign of Cancer, you give yourself freely to the world and will always be on hand if anyone is in trouble or needs the special touch you can bring to almost any problem. Behaving in this way is the biggest part of what you are and so people come to rely on you very heavily. Like Libra you can see both sides of any coin and you exhibit the Libran tendency to jump about from one foot to the other when it is necessary to make decisions relating to your own life. This is not usually the case when you are dealing with others, however, because the cooler and more detached qualities of Cancer will show through in these circumstances.

It would be fair to say that you do not deal with routines as well as Cancer alone might do and you need a degree of variety in your life. In your case this possibly comes in the form of travel, which can be distant and of long duration. It isn't unusual for people who have this zodiac combination to end up living abroad, though even this does little to prevent you from getting itchy feet from time to time. In relationships you show an original quality that keeps the relationship young, fresh and working well.

Cancer with Scorpio Ascendant

There are few more endearing zodiac combinations than this. Both signs are Watery in nature and show a desire to work on behalf of humanity as a whole. The world sees you as being genuinely caring, full of sympathy for anyone in trouble and always ready to lend a hand when it is needed. You are a loyal friend, a great supporter of the oppressed and a lover of home and family. In a work sense you are capable and command respect from your colleagues, even though this comes about courtesy of your quiet competence, and not as a result of anything that you might happen to say or do.

But we should not get too carried away with external factors, or the way that others see you. Inside you are a boiling pool of emotion. You feel more strongly, love more deeply and hurt more fully than any other combination of the Water signs. Even those who think that they know you really well would get a shock if they could take a stroll around the deeper recesses of your mind. Although these facts are true, they may be rather beside the point because the truth of your passion, commitment and deep convictions may only surface fully half a dozen times in your life. The fact is that you are a very private person at heart and you don't know how to be any other way.

Cancer with Sagittarius Ascendant

You have far more drive, enthusiasm and get-up-and-go than would seem to be the case for Cancer when taken alone, but all of this is tempered with a certain quiet compassion that probably makes you the best sort of Sagittarian too. It's true that you don't like to be on your own or to retire into your shell quite as much as the Crab usually does, though there are, even in your case, occasions when this is going to be necessary. Absolute concentration can sometimes be a problem to you, though this is hardly likely to be the case when you are dealing with matters relating to your home or family, both of which reign supreme in your thinking. Always loving and kind, you are a social animal and enjoy being out there in the real world, expressing the deeper opinions of Cancer much more readily than would often be the case with other combinations relating to the sign of the Crab.

Personality is not lacking, and you tend to be very popular, not least because you are the fountain of good and practical advice. You want to get things done, and retain a practical approach to most situations which is the envy of many of the people you meet. As a parent you are second to none, combining common sense, dignity and a sensible approach. To balance this you stay young enough to understand children.

Cancer with Capricorn Ascendant

The single most important factor here is the practical ability to get things done and to see any task, professional or personal, through to the end. Since half this combination is Cancer, that also means expounding much of your energy on behalf of others. There isn't a charity in the world that would fail to recognise what a potent combination this is when it comes to the very concrete side of offering help and assistance. Many of your ideas hold water and you don't set off on abortive journeys of any kind, simply because you tend to get the ground rules fixed in your mind first.

On a more personal level you can be rather hard to get to know, because both these signs have a deep quality and a tendency to keep things in the dark. The mystery may only serve to encourage people to try and get to know you better. As a result you could attract a host of admirers, many of whom would wish to form romantic attachments. This may prove to be irrelevant, however, because once you give your heart, you tend to be loyal and would only change your mind if you were pushed into doing so. Prolonged periods of inactivity don't do you any good and it is sensible for you to keep on the move, even though your progress in life is measured and very steady.

Cancer with Aquarius Ascendant

The truly original spark, for which the sign of Aquarius is famed, can only enhance the caring qualities of Cancer, and is also inclined to bring the Crab out of its shell to a much greater extent than would be the case with certain other zodiac combinations. Aquarius is a party animal and never arrives without something interesting to say, which is doubly so when the reservoir of emotion and consideration that is Cancer is feeding the tap. Your nature can be rather confusing, even for you to deal with, but you are inspirational, bright, charming and definitely fun to be around.

The Cancer element in your nature means that you care about your home and the people to whom you are related. You are also a good and loyal friend, who would keep attachments for much longer than could be expected for Aquarius alone. You love to travel and can be expected to make many journeys to far-off places during your life. Some attention will have to be paid to your health because you are capable of burning up masses of nervous energy, often without getting the periods of rest and contemplation that are essential to the deeper qualities of the sign of Cancer. Nevertheless you have determination, resilience and a refreshing attitude that lifts the spirits of the people in your vicinity.

Cancer with Pisces Ascendant

A deep, double Water-sign combination, this one, and it might serve to make you a very misunderstood, though undoubtedly popular, individual. You are keen to make a good impression, probably too keen under certain circumstances, and you do everything you can to help others, even if you don't know them very well. It's true that you are deeply sensitive and quite easily brought to tears by the suffering of this most imperfect world that we inhabit. Fatigue can be a problem, though this is nullified to some extent by the fact that

21

you can withdraw completely into the deep recesses of your own mind when it becomes necessary to do so.

You may not be the most gregarious person in the world, simply because it isn't easy for you to put your most important considerations into words. This is easier when you are in the company of people you know and trust, though even trust is a commodity that is difficult for you to find, particularly since you may have been hurt by being too willing to share your thoughts early in life. With age comes wisdom and maturity and the older you are, the better you will learn to handle this potent and demanding combination. You will never go short of either friends or would-be lovers, and may be one of the most magnetic types of both Cancer and Pisces.

Cancer with Aries Ascendant

The main problem that you experience in life shows itself as a direct result of the meshing of these two very different zodiac signs. At heart Aries needs to dominate, whereas Cancer shows a desire to nurture. All too often the result can be a protective arm that is so strong that nobody could possibly get out from under it. Lighten your own load, and that of those you care for, by being willing to sit back and watch others please themselves a little. You might think that you know best, and your heart is clearly in the right place, but try and realise what life can be like when someone is always on hand to tell you that they know better than you do.

But in a way this is a little severe, because you are fairly intuitive and your instincts will rarely lead you astray. Nobody could ask for a better partner or parent than you would be, though they might request a slightly less attentive one. In matters of work you are conscientious, and are probably best suited to a job that means sorting out the kind of mess that humanity is so good at creating. You probably spend your spare time untangling balls of wool, though you are quite sporting too and could even make the Olympics. Once there you would not win however, because you would be too concerned about all the other competitors!

Cancer with Taurus Ascendant

Your main aim in life seems to be to look after everyone and everything that you come across. From your deepest and most enduring human love, right down to the birds in the park, you really do care and you show that natural affection in many different ways. Your nature is sensitive and you are easily moved to tears, though this does not prevent you from pitching in and doing practical things to assist at just about any level. There is a danger that you could stifle those same people whom you set out to assist, and people with this zodiac combination are often unwilling, or unable, to allow their children to grow and leave the nest. More time spent considering what suits you would be no bad thing, but the problem is that you find it almost impossible to imagine any situation that doesn't involve your most basic need, which is to nurture.

You appear not to possess a selfish streak, though it sometimes turns out that in being certain that you understand the needs of the world, you are nevertheless treading on their toes. This eventual realisation can be very painful, but it isn't a stick with which you should beat yourself because at heart you are one of the kindest people imaginable. Your sense of fair play means that you are a quiet social reformer at heart.

Cancer with Gemini Ascendant

Many astrologers would say that this is a happy combination because some of the more flighty qualities of Gemini are somewhat modified by the steady influence of Cancer the Crab. To all intents and purposes you show the friendly and gregarious qualities of Gemini, but there is a thoughtful and even sometimes a serious quality that would not be present in Gemini when taken alone. Looking after people is high on your list of priorities and you do this most of the time. This is made possible because you have greater staying power than Gemini is usually said to possess and you can easily see fairly complicated situations through to their conclusion without becoming bored on the way.

The chances are that you will have many friends and that these people show great concern for your well-being, because you choose them carefully and show them a great deal of consideration. However, you will still be on the receiving end of gossip on occasions, and need to treat such situations with a healthy pinch of salt. Like all part-Geminis your nervous system is not as strong as you would wish to believe and family pressures in particular can put great strain on you. Activities of all kinds take your fancy and many people with this combination are attracted to sailing or wind surfing.

THE MOON AND THE PART IT PLAYS IN YOUR LIFE

In astrology the Moon is probably the single most important heavenly body after the Sun. Its unique position, as partner to the Earth on its journey around the solar system, means that the Moon appears to pass through the signs of the zodiac extremely quickly. The zodiac position of the Moon at the time of your birth plays a great part in personal character and is especially significant in the build-up of your emotional nature.

Sun Moon Cycles

The first lunar cycle deals with the part the position of the Moon plays relative to your Sun sign. I have made the fluctuations of this pattern easy for you to understand by means of a simple cyclic graph. It appears on the first page of each 'Your Month At A Glance', under the title 'Highs and Lows'. The graph displays the lunar cycle and you will soon learn to understand how its movements have a bearing on your level of energy and your abilities.

Your Own Moon Sign

Discovering the position of the Moon at the time of your birth has always been notoriously difficult because tracking the complex zodiac positions of the Moon is not easy. This process has been reduced to three simple stages with Old Moore's unique Lunar Tables. A breakdown of the Moon's zodiac positions can be found from page 28 onwards, so that once you know what your Moon Sign is, you can see what part this plays in the overall build-up of your personal character.

If you follow the instructions on the next page you will soon be able to work out exactly what zodiac sign the Moon occupied on the day that you were born and you can then go on to compare the reading for this position with those of your Sun sign and your Ascendant. It is partly the comparison between these three important positions that goes towards making you the unique individual you are.

HOW TO DISCOVER YOUR MOON SIGN

This is a three-stage process. You may need a pen and a piece of paper but if you follow the instructions below the process should only take a minute or so.

STAGE 1 First of all you need to know the Moon Age at the time of your birth. If you look at Moon Table 1, on page 26, you will find all the years between 1916 and 2014 down the left side. Find the year of your birth and then trace across to the right to the month of your birth. Where the two intersect you will find a number. This is the date of the New Moon in the month that you were born. You now need to count forward the number of days between the New Moon and your own birthday. For example, if the New Moon in the month of your birth was shown as being the 6th and you were born on the 20th, your Moon Age Day would be 14. If the New Moon in the month of your birth came after your birthday, you need to count forward from the New Moon in the previous month. Whatever the result, jot this number down so that you do not forget it.

STAGE 2 Take a look at Moon Table 2 on page 27. Down the left hand column look for the date of your birth. Now trace across to the month of your birth. Where the two meet you will find a letter. Copy this letter down alongside your Moon Age Day.

STAGE 3 Moon Table 3 on page 27 will supply you with the zodiac sign the Moon occupied on the day of your birth. Look for your Moon Age Day down the left hand column and then for the letter you found in Stage 2. Where the two converge you will find a zodiac sign and this is the sign occupied by the Moon on the day that you were born.

Your Zodiac Moon Sign Explained

You will find a profile of all zodiac Moon Signs on pages 28 to 31, showing in yet another way how astrology helps to make you into the individual that you are. In each daily entry of the Astral Diary you can find the zodiac position of the Moon for every day of the year. This also allows you to discover your lunar birthdays. Since the Moon passes through all the signs of the zodiac in about a month, you can expect something like twelve lunar birthdays each year. At these times you are likely to be emotionally steady and able to make the sort of decisions that have real, lasting value.

Moon Table 1

YEAR	MAY	JUN	JUL	YEAR	MAY	JUN	JUL	YEAR	MAY	JUN	JUL
1917	20	19	18	1950	17	15	15	1983	12	11	10
1918	10	8	8	1951	6	4	4	1984	1/30	29	28
1919	29	27	27	1952	23	22	22	1985	19	18	17
1920	18	16	15	1953	13	11	11	1986	8	7	7
1921	7	6	5	1954	2	1/30	29	1987	27	26	25
1922	26	25	24	1955	21	20	19	1988	15	14	13
1923	15	14	14	1956	10	8	8	1989	5	3	3
1924	3	2	2/31	1957	29	27	27	1990	24	22	22
1925	22	21	20	1958	18	17	16	1991	13	11	11
1926	11	10	9	1959	7	6	6	1992	2	1/30	29
1927	2/31	29	28	1960	26	24	24	1993	21	19	19
1928	19	18	17	1961	14	13	12	1994	10	8	8
1929	9	7	6	1962	4	2	1/31	1995	29	27	27
1930	28	26	25	1963	23	21	20	1996	18	17	15
1931	17	16	15	1964	11	10	9	1997	6	5	4
1932	5	4	3	1965	1/30	29	28	1998	25	24	23
1933	24	23	22	1966	19	18	17	1999	15	13	13
1934	13	12	11	1967	8	7	7	2000	4	2	1/31
1935	2	1/30	30	1968	27	26	25	2001	23	21	20
1936	20	19	18	1969	15	14	13	2002	12	10	9
1937	10	8	8	1970	6	4	4	2003	1/30	29	28
1938	29	27	27	1971	24	22	22	2004	18	16	16
1939	19	17	16	1972	13	11	11	2005	8	6	6
1940	7	6	5	1973	2	1/30	29	2006	27	26	25
1941	26	24	24	1974	21	20	19	2007	17	15	15
1942	15	13	13	1975	11	9	9	2008	5	4	3
1943	4	2	2	1976	29	27	27	2009	25	23	22
1944	22	20	20	1977	18	16	16	2010	14	12	12
1945	11	10	9	1978	7	5	5	2011	3	2	2
1946	1/30	29	28	1979	26	24	24	2012	20	19	19
1947	19	18	17	1980	14	13	12	2013	10	8	7
1948	9	7	6	1981	4	2	1/31	2014	29	27	25
1949	27	26	25	1982	21	21	20	2015	18	17	16

Table 2

DAY	JUN	JUL
1	O	R
2	P	R
3	P	S
4	P	S
5	P	S
6	P	S
7	P	S
8	P	S
9	P	S
10	P	S
11	P	S
12	Q	S
13	Q	T
14	Q	T
15	Q	T
16	Q	T
17	Q	T
18	Q	T
19	Q	T
20	Q	T
21	Q	T
22	R	T
23	R	T
24	R	U
25	R	U
26	R	U
27	R	U
28	R	U
29	R	U
30	R	U
31	–	U

Table 3

M/D	O	P	Q	R	S	T	U
0	GE	GE	CA	CA	CA	LE	LE
1	GE	CA	CA	CA	LE	LE	LE
2	CA	CA	CA	LE	LE	LE	VI
3	CA	CA	LE	LE	LE	VI	VI
4	LE	LE	LE	LE	VI	VI	LI
5	LE	LE	VI	VI	VI	LI	LI
6	VI	VI	VI	VI	LI	LI	LI
7	VI	VI	LI	LI	LI	LI	SC
8	VI	VI	LI	LI	LI	SC	SC
9	LI	LI	SC	SC	SC	SC	SA
10	LI	LI	SC	SC	SC	SA	SA
11	SC	SC	SC	SA	SA	SA	CP
12	SC	SC	SA	SA‘	SA	SA	CP
13	SC	SA	SA	SA	SA	CP	CP
14	SA	SA	SA	CP	CP	CP	AQ
15	SA	SA	CP	CP	CP	AQ	AQ
16	CP	CP	CP	AQ	AQ	AQ	AQ
17	CP	CP	CP	AQ	AQ	AQ	PI
18	CP	CP	AQ	AQ	AQ	PI	PI
19	AQ	AQ	AQ	PI	PI	PI	PI
20	AQ	AQ	PI	PI	PI	AR	AR
21	AQ	PI	PI	PI	AR	AR	AR
22	PI	PI	PI	AR	AR	AR	TA
23	PI	PI	AR	AR	AR	TA	TA
24	PI	AR	AR	AR	TA	TA	TA
25	AR	AR	TA	TA	TA	GE	GE
26	AR	TA	TA	TA	GE	GE	GE
27	TA	TA	TA	GE	GE	GE	CA
28	TA	TA	GE	GE	GE	CA	CA
29	TA	GE	GE	GE	CA	CA	CA

AR = Aries, TA = Taurus, GE = Gemini, CA = Cancer, LE = Leo, VI = Virgo, LI = Libra, SC = Scorpio, SA = Sagittarius, CP = Capricorn, AQ = Aquarius, PI = Pisces

MOON SIGNS

Moon in Aries

You have a strong imagination, courage, determination and a desire to do things in your own way and forge your own path through life.

Originality is a key attribute; you are seldom stuck for ideas although your mind is changeable and you could take the time to focus on individual tasks. Often quick-tempered, you take orders from few people and live life at a fast pace. Avoid health problems by taking regular time out for rest and relaxation.

Emotionally, it is important that you talk to those you are closest to and work out your true feelings. Once you discover that people are there to help, there is less necessity for you to do everything yourself.

Moon in Taurus

The Moon in Taurus gives you a courteous and friendly manner, which means you are likely to have many friends.

The good things in life mean a lot to you, as Taurus is an Earth sign that delights in experiences which please the senses. Hence you are probably a lover of good food and drink, which may in turn mean you need to keep an eye on the bathroom scales, especially as looking good is also important to you.

Emotionally you are fairly stable and you stick by your own standards. Taureans do not respond well to change. Intuition also plays an important part in your life.

Moon in Gemini

You have a warm-hearted character, sympathetic and eager to help others. At times reserved, you can also be articulate and chatty: this is part of the paradox of Gemini, which always brings duplicity to the nature. You are interested in current affairs, have a good intellect, and are good company and likely to have many friends. Most of your friends have a high opinion of you and would be ready to defend you should the need arise. However, this is usually unnecessary, as you are quite capable of defending yourself in any verbal confrontation.

Travel is important to your inquisitive mind and you find intellectual stimulus in mixing with people from different cultures. You also gain much from reading, writing and the arts but you do need plenty of rest and relaxation in order to avoid fatigue.

Moon in Cancer

The Moon in Cancer at the time of birth is a fortunate position as Cancer is the Moon's natural home. This means that the qualities of compassion and understanding given by the Moon are especially enhanced in your nature, and you are friendly and sociable and cope well with emotional pressures. You cherish home and family life, and happily do the domestic tasks. Your surroundings are important to you and you hate squalor and filth. You are likely to have a love of music and poetry.

Your basic character, although at times changeable like the Moon itself, depends on symmetry. You aim to make your surroundings comfortable and harmonious, for yourself and those close to you.

Moon in Leo

The best qualities of the Moon and Leo come together to make you warmhearted, fair, ambitious and self-confident. With good organisational abilities, you invariably rise to a position of responsibility in your chosen career. This is fortunate as you don't enjoy being an 'also-ran' and would rather be an important part of a small organisation than a menial in a large one.

You should be lucky in love, and happy, provided you put in the effort to make a comfortable home for yourself and those close to you. It is likely that you will have a love of pleasure, sport, music and literature. Life brings you many rewards, most of them as a direct result of your own efforts, although you may be luckier than average and ready to make the best of any situation.

Moon in Virgo

You are endowed with good mental abilities and a keen receptive memory, but you are never ostentatious or pretentious. Naturally quite reserved, you still have many friends, especially of the opposite sex. Marital relationships must be discussed carefully and worked at so that they remain harmonious, as personal attachments can be a problem if you do not give them your full attention.

Talented and persevering, you possess artistic qualities and are a good homemaker. Earning your honours through genuine merit, you work long and hard towards your objectives but show little pride in your achievements. Many short journeys will be undertaken in your life.

Moon in Libra

With the Moon in Libra you are naturally popular and make friends easily. People like you, probably more than you realise, you bring fun to a party and are a natural diplomat. For all its good points, Libra is not the most stable of astrological signs and, as a result, your emotions can be a little unstable too. Therefore, although the Moon in Libra is said to be good for love and marriage, your Sun sign and Rising sign will have an important effect on your emotional and loving qualities.

You must remember to relate to others in your decision-making. Co-operation is crucial because Libra represents the 'balance' of life that can only be achieved through harmonious relationships. Conformity is not easy for you because Libra, an Air sign, likes its independence.

Moon in Scorpio

Some people might call you pushy. In fact, all you really want to do is to live life to the full and protect yourself and your family from the pressures of life. Take care to avoid giving the impression of being sarcastic or impulsive and use your energies wisely and constructively.

You have great courage and you invariably achieve your goals by force of personality and sheer effort. You are fond of mystery and are good at predicting the outcome of situations and events. Travel experiences can be beneficial to you.

You may experience problems if you do not take time to examine your motives in a relationship, and also if you allow jealousy, always a feature of Scorpio, to cloud your judgement.

Moon in Sagittarius

The Moon in Sagittarius helps to make you a generous individual with humanitarian qualities and a kind heart. Restlessness may be intrinsic as your mind is seldom still. Perhaps because of this, you have a need for change that could lead you to several major moves during your adult life. You are not afraid to stand your ground when you know your judgement is right, you speak directly and have good intuition.

At work you are quick, efficient and versatile and so you make an ideal employee. You need work to be intellectually demanding and do not enjoy tedious routines.

In relationships, you anger quickly if faced with stupidity or deception, though you are just as quick to forgive and forget. Emotionally, there are times when your heart rules your head.

Moon in Capricorn

The Moon in Capricorn makes you popular and likely to come into the public eye in some way. The watery Moon is not entirely comfortable in the Earth sign of Capricorn and this may lead to some difficulties in the early years of life. An initial lack of creative ability and indecision must be overcome before the true qualities of patience and perseverance inherent in Capricorn can show through.

You have good administrative ability and are a capable worker, and if you are careful you can accumulate wealth. But you must be cautious and take professional advice in partnerships, as you are open to deception. You may be interested in social or welfare work, which suit your organisational skills and sympathy for others.

Moon in Aquarius

The Moon in Aquarius makes you an active and agreeable person with a friendly, easy-going nature. Sympathetic to the needs of others, you flourish in a laid-back atmosphere. You are broad-minded, fair and open to suggestion, although sometimes you have an unconventional quality which others can find hard to understand.

You are interested in the strange and curious, and in old articles and places. You enjoy trips to these places and gain much from them. Political, scientific and educational work interests you and you might choose a career in science or technology.

Money-wise, you make gains through innovation and concentration and Lunar Aquarians often tackle more than one job at a time. In love you are kind and honest.

Moon in Pisces

You have a kind, sympathetic nature, somewhat retiring at times, but you always take account of others' feelings and help when you can.

Personal relationships may be problematic, but as life goes on you can learn from your experiences and develop a better understanding of yourself and the world around you.

You have a fondness for travel, appreciate beauty and harmony and hate disorder and strife. You may be fond of literature and would make a good writer or speaker yourself. You have a creative imagination and may come across as an incurable romantic. You have strong intuition, maybe bordering on a mediumistic quality, which sets you apart from the mass. You may not be rich in cash terms, but your personal gifts are worth more than gold.

CANCER IN LOVE

Discover how compatible you are with people from the same and other signs of the zodiac. Five stars equals a match made in heaven!

Cancer meets Cancer

This match will work because the couple share a mutual understanding. Cancerians are very kind people who also respond well to kindness from others, so a double Cancer match can almost turn into a mutual appreciation society! But this will not lead to selfish hedonism, as the Crab takes in order to give more. There is an impressive physical, emotional and spiritual meeting of minds, which will lead to a successful and inspiring pairing in its own low-key and deeply sensitive way. Star rating: ★★★★★

Cancer meets Leo

This relationship will usually be directed by Leo more towards its own needs than Cancer's. However, the Crab will willingly play second fiddle to more progressive and bossy types as it is deeply emotional and naturally supportive. Leo is bright, caring, magnanimous and protective and so, as long as it isn't over-assertive, this could be a good match. On the surface, Cancer appears the more conventional of the two, but Leo will discover, to its delight, that it can be unusual and quirky. Star rating: ★★★★

Cancer meets Virgo

This match has little chance of success, for fairly simple reasons: Cancer's generous affection will be submerged by the Virgoan depths, not because Virgo is uncaring but because it expresses itself so differently. As both signs are naturally quiet, things might become a bit boring. They would be mutually supportive, possibly financially successful and have a very tidy house, but they won't share much sparkle, enthusiasm, risk-taking or passion. If this pair were stranded on a desert island, they might live at different ends of it. Star rating: ★★

Cancer meets Libra

Almost anyone can get on with Libra, which is one of the most adaptable signs of them all. But being adaptable does not always lead to fulfilment, and a successful match here will require a quiet Libran and a slightly more progressive Cancerian than the norm. Both signs are pleasant, polite and like domestic order, but Libra may find Cancer too emotional and perhaps lacking in vibrancy, while Libra, on the other hand, may be a little too flighty for steady Cancer. Star rating: ***

Cancer meets Scorpio

This match is potentially a great success, a fact which is often a mystery to astrologers. Some feel it is due to the compatibility of the Water element, but it could also come from a mixture of similarity and difference in the personalities. Scorpio is partly ruled by Mars, which gives it a deep, passionate, dominant and powerful side. Cancerians generally like and respect this amalgam, and recognise something there that they would like to adopt themselves. On the other side of the coin, Scorpio needs love and emotional security which Cancer offers generously. Star rating: *****

Cancer meets Sagittarius

Although probably not an immediate success, there is hope for this couple. It's hard to see how this pair could get together, because they have few mutual interests. Sagittarius is always on the go, loves a hectic social life and dances the night away. Cancer prefers the cinema or a concert. But, having met, Cancer will appreciate the Archer's happy and cheerful nature, while Sagittarius finds Cancer alluring and intriguing and, as the saying goes, opposites attract. A long-term relationship would focus on commitment to family, with Cancer leading this area. Star rating: ***

Cancer meets Capricorn

Just about the only thing this pair have in common is the fact that both signs begin with 'Ca'! Some signs of the zodiac are instigators and some are reactors, and both the Crab and the Goat are reactors. Consequently, they both need incentives from their partners but won't find it in each other and, with neither side taking the initiative, there's a spark missing. Cancer and Capricorn do think alike in some ways and so, if they can find their spark or common purpose, they can be as happy as anyone. It's just rather unlikely. Star rating: **

Cancer meets Aquarius

Cancer is often attracted to Aquarius and, as Aquarius is automatically on the side of anyone who fancies it, so there is the potential for something good here. Cancer loves Aquarius' devil-may-care approach to life, but also recognises and seeks to strengthen the basic lack of self-confidence that all Air signs try so hard to keep secret. Both signs are natural travellers and are quite adventurous. Their family life would be unusual, even peculiar, but friends would recognise a caring, sharing household with many different interests shared by people genuinely in love. Star rating: ***

Cancer meets Pisces

This is likely to be a very successful match. Cancer and Pisces are both Water signs, and are both deep, sensitive and very caring. Pisces loves deeply, and Cancer wants to be loved. There will be few fireworks here, and a very quiet house. But that doesn't mean that either love or action is lacking – the latter of which is just behind closed doors. Family and children are important to both signs and both are prepared to work hard, but Pisces is the more restless of the two and needs the support and security that Cancer offers. Star rating: *****

Cancer meets Aries

A potentially one-sided pairing, it often appears that the Cancerian is brow-beaten by the far more dominant Arian. So much depends on the patience of the Cancerian individual, because if good psychology is present – who knows? But beware, Aries, you may find your partner too passive, and constantly having to take the lead can be wearing – even for you. A prolonged trial period would be advantageous, as the match could easily go either way. When it does work, though, this relationship is usually contented. Star rating: ***

Cancer meets Taurus

This pair will have the tidiest house in the street – every stick of furniture in place, and no errant blade of grass daring to spoil the lawn. But things inside the relationship might not be quite so ship-shape as both signs need, but don't offer, encouragement. There's plenty of affection, but few incentives for mutual progress. This might not prevent material success, but an enduring relationship isn't based on money alone. Passion is essential, and both parties need to realise and aim for that.
Star rating: **

Cancer meets Gemini

This is often a very good match. Cancer is a very caring sign and quite adaptable. Geminis are untidy, have butterfly minds and are usually full of a thousand different schemes which Cancerians take in their stride and even relish. They can often be the 'wind beneath the wings' of their Gemini partners. In return, Gemini can eradicate some of the Cancerian emotional insecurity and will be more likely to be faithful in thought, word and deed to Cancer than to almost any other sign.
Star rating: ****

VENUS:
THE PLANET OF LOVE

If you look up at the sky around sunset or sunrise you will often see Venus in close attendance to the Sun. It is arguably one of the most beautiful sights of all and there is little wonder that historically it became associated with the goddess of love. But although Venus does play an important part in the way you view love and in the way others see you romantically, this is only one of the spheres of influence that it enjoys in your overall character.

Venus has a part to play in the more cultured side of your life and has much to do with your appreciation of art, literature, music and general creativity. Even the way you look is responsive to the part of the zodiac that Venus occupied at the start of your life, though this fact is also down to your Sun sign and Ascending sign. If, at the time you were born, Venus occupied one of the more gregarious zodiac signs, you will be more likely to wear your heart on your sleeve, as well as to be more attracted to entertainment, social gatherings and good company. If on the other hand Venus occupied a quiet zodiac sign at the time of your birth, you would tend to be more retiring and less willing to shine in public situations.

It's good to know what part the planet Venus plays in your life, for it can have a great bearing on the way you appear to the rest of the world and since we all have to mix with others, you can learn to make the very best of what Venus has to offer you.

One of the great complications in the past has always been trying to establish exactly what zodiac position Venus enjoyed when you were born, because the planet is notoriously difficult to track. However, I have solved that problem by creating a table that is exclusive to your Sun sign, which you will find on the following page.

Establishing your Venus sign could not be easier. Just look up the year of your birth on the page opposite and you will see a sign of the zodiac. This was the sign that Venus occupied in the period covered by your sign in that year. If Venus occupied more than one sign during the period, this is indicated by the date on which the sign changed, and the name of the new sign. For instance, if you were born in 1950, Venus was in Taurus until the 27th June, after which time it was in Gemini. If you were born before 27th June your Venus sign is Taurus, if you were born on or after 27th June, your Venus sign is Gemini. Once you have established the position of Venus at the time of your birth, you can then look in the pages which follow to see how this has a bearing on your life as a whole.

1917 CANCER / 5.7 LEO
1918 TAURUS / 29.6 GEMINI
1919 LEO / 8.7 VIRGO
1920 GEMINI / 25.6 CANCER /
    18.7 LEO
1921 TAURUS / 8.7 GEMINI
1922 LEO / 15.7 VIRGO
1923 GEMINI / 10.7 CANCER
1924 CANCER
1925 CANCER / 4.7 LEO
1926 TAURUS / 28.6 GEMINI
1927 LEO / 8.7 VIRGO
1928 GEMINI / 24.6 CANCER /
    18.7 LEO
1929 TAURUS / 8.7 GEMINI
1930 LEO / 15.7 VIRGO
1931 GEMINI / 10.7 CANCER
1932 CANCER
1933 CANCER / 4.7 LEO
1934 TAURUS / 27.6 GEMINI
1935 LEO / 8.7 VIRGO
1936 GEMINI / 24.6 CANCER /
    17.7 LEO
1937 TAURUS / 8.7 GEMINI
1938 LEO / 14.7 VIRGO
1939 GEMINI / 9.7 CANCER
1940 CANCER / 13.7 GEMINI
1941 CANCER / 3.7 LEO
1942 TAURUS / 27.6 GEMINI
1943 LEO / 9.7 VIRGO
1944 GEMINI / 23.6 CANCER /
    17.7 LEO
1945 TAURUS / 7.7 GEMINI
1946 LEO / 14.7 VIRGO
1947 GEMINI / 9.7 CANCER
1948 CANCER / 6.7 GEMINI
1949 CANCER / 2.7 LEO
1950 TAURUS / 27.6 GEMINI
1951 LEO / 9.7 VIRGO
1952 GEMINI / 23.6 CANCER /
    17.7 LEO
1953 TAURUS / 7.7 GEMINI
1954 LEO / 13.7 VIRGO
1955 GEMINI / 8.7 CANCER
1956 CANCER / 29.6 GEMINI
1957 CANCER / 1.7 LEO
1958 TAURUS / 26.6 GEMINI
1959 LEO / 9.7 VIRGO
1960 CANCER / 16.7 LEO
1961 TAURUS / 7.7 GEMINI
1962 LEO / 13.7 VIRGO
1963 GEMINI / 8.7 CANCER
1964 CANCER / 22.6 GEMINI
1965 CANCER / 1.7 LEO
1966 TAURUS / 26.6 GEMINI
1967 LEO / 10.7 VIRGO

1968 CANCER / 16.7 LEO
1969 TAURUS / 6.7 GEMINI
1970 LEO / 13.7 VIRGO
1971 GEMINI / 7.7 CANCER
1972 CANCER / 22.6 GEMINI
1973 CANCER / 30.6 LEO
1974 TAURUS / 26.6 GEMINI /
    22.7 CANCER
1975 LEO / 10.7 VIRGO
1976 CANCER / 15.7 LEO
1977 TAURUS / 6.7 GEMINI
1978 LEO / 12.7 VIRGO
1979 GEMINI / 7.7 CANCER
1980 CANCER / 22.6 GEMINI
1981 CANCER / 30.6 LEO
1982 TAURUS / 26.6 GEMINI /
    21.7 CANCER
1983 LEO / 10.7 VIRGO
1984 CANCER / 15.7 LEO
1985 TAURUS / 6.7 GEMINI
1986 LEO / 12.7 VIRGO
1987 GEMINI / 6.7 CANCER
1988 CANCER / 22.6 GEMINI
1989 CANCER / 29.6 LEO
1990 TAURUS / 25.6 GEMINI /
    20.7 CANCER
1991 LEO / 11.7 VIRGO
1992 CANCER / 14.7 LEO
1993 TAURUS / 5.7 GEMINI
1994 LEO / 11.7 VIRGO
1995 GEMINI / 5.7 CANCER
1996 CANCER / 22.6 GEMINI
1997 CANCER / 29.6 LEO
1998 TAURUS / 25.6 GEMINI /
    20.7 CANCER
1999 LEO / 11.7 VIRGO
2000 CANCER / 14.7 LEO
2001 TAURUS / 5.7 GEMINI
2002 LEO / 11.7 VIRGO
2003 GEMINI / 5.7 CANCER
2004 CANCER / 22.6 GEMINI
2005 CANCER / 29.6 LEO
2006 TAURUS / 25.6 GEMINI /
    20.7 CANCER
2007 LEO / 11.7 VIRGO
2008 CANCER / 14.7 LEO
2009 TAURUS / 5.7 GEMINI
2010 LEO / 11.7 VIRGO
2011 GEMINI / 5.7 CANCER
2012 CANCER / 22.6 GEMINI
2013 TAURUS / 25.6 GEMINI /
    20.7 CANCER
2014 TAURUS / 25.6 GEMINI /
    20.7 CANCER
2015 LEO / 11.7 VIRGO

VENUS THROUGH THE ZODIAC SIGNS

Venus in Aries

Amongst other things, the position of Venus in Aries indicates a fondness for travel, music and all creative pursuits. Your nature tends to be affectionate and you would try not to create confusion or difficulty for others if it could be avoided. Many people with this planetary position have a great love of the theatre, and mental stimulation is of the greatest importance. Early romantic attachments are common with Venus in Aries, so it is very important to establish a genuine sense of romantic continuity. Early marriage is not recommended, especially if it is based on sympathy. You may give your heart a little too readily on occasions.

Venus in Taurus

You are capable of very deep feelings and your emotions tend to last for a very long time. This makes you a trusting partner and lover, whose constancy is second to none. In life you are precise and careful and always try to do things the right way. Although this means an ordered life, which you are comfortable with, it can also lead you to be rather too fussy for your own good. Despite your pleasant nature, you are very fixed in your opinions and quite able to speak your mind. Others are attracted to you and historical astrologers always quoted this position of Venus as being very fortunate in terms of marriage. However, if you find yourself involved in a failed relationship, it could take you a long time to trust again.

Venus in Gemini

As with all associations related to Gemini, you tend to be quite versatile, anxious for change and intelligent in your dealings with the world at large. You may gain money from more than one source but you are equally good at spending it. There is an inference here that you are a good communicator, via either the written or the spoken word, and you love to be in the company of interesting people. Always on the look-out for culture, you may also be very fond of music, and love to indulge the curious and cultured side of your nature. In romance you tend to have more than one relationship and could find yourself associated with someone who has previously been a friend or even a distant relative.

Venus in Cancer

You often stay close to home because you are very fond of family and enjoy many of your most treasured moments when you are with those you love. Being naturally sympathetic, you will always do anything you can to support those around you, even people you hardly know at all. This charitable side of your nature is your most noticeable trait and is one of the reasons why others are naturally so fond of you. Being receptive and in some cases even psychic, you can see through to the soul of most of those with whom you come into contact. You may not commence too many romantic attachments but when you do give your heart, it tends to be unconditionally.

Venus in Leo

It must become quickly obvious to almost anyone you meet that you are kind, sympathetic and yet determined enough to stand up for anyone or anything that is truly important to you. Bright and sunny, you warm the world with your natural enthusiasm and would rarely do anything to hurt those around you, or at least not intentionally. In romance you are ardent and sincere, though some may find your style just a little overpowering. Gains come through your contacts with other people and this could be especially true with regard to romance, for love and money often come hand in hand for those who were born with Venus in Leo. People claim to understand you, though you are more complex than you seem.

Venus in Virgo

Your nature could well be fairly quiet no matter what your Sun sign might be, though this fact often manifests itself as an inner peace and would not prevent you from being basically sociable. Some delays and even the odd disappointment in love cannot be ruled out with this planetary position, though it's a fact that you will usually find the happiness you look for in the end. Catapulting yourself into romantic entanglements that you know to be rather ill-advised is not sensible, and it would be better to wait before you committed yourself exclusively to any one person. It is the essence of your nature to serve the world at large and through doing so it is possible that you will attract money at some stage in your life.

Venus in Libra

Venus is very comfortable in Libra and bestows upon those people who have this planetary position a particular sort of kindness that is easy to recognise. This is a very good position for all sorts of friendships and also for romantic attachments that usually bring much joy into your life. Few individuals with Venus in Libra would avoid marriage and since you are capable of great depths of love, it is likely that you will find a contented personal life. You like to mix with people of integrity and intelligence but don't take kindly to scruffy surroundings or work that means getting your hands too dirty. Careful speculation, good business dealings and money through marriage all seem fairly likely.

Venus in Scorpio

You are quite open and tend to spend money quite freely, even on those occasions when you don't have very much. Although your intentions are always good, there are times when you get yourself in to the odd scrape and this can be particularly true when it comes to romance, which you may come to late or from a rather unexpected direction. Certainly you have the power to be happy and to make others contented on the way, but you find the odd stumbling block on your journey through life and it could seem that you have to work harder than those around you. As a result of this, you gain a much deeper understanding of the true value of personal happiness than many people ever do, and are likely to achieve true contentment in the end.

Venus in Sagittarius

You are lighthearted, cheerful and always able to see the funny side of any situation. These facts enhance your popularity, which is especially high with members of the opposite sex. You should never have to look too far to find romantic interest in your life, though it is just possible that you might be too willing to commit yourself before you are certain that the person in question is right for you. Part of the problem here extends to other areas of life too. The fact is that you like variety in everything and so can tire of situations that fail to offer it. All the same, if you choose wisely and learn to understand your restless side, then great happiness can be yours.

Venus in Capricorn

The most notable trait that comes from Venus in this position is that it makes you trustworthy and able to take on all sorts of responsibilities in life. People are instinctively fond of you and love you all the more because you are always ready to help those who are in any form of need. Social and business popularity can be yours and there is a magnetic quality to your nature that is particularly attractive in a romantic sense. Anyone who wants a partner for a lover, a spouse and a good friend too would almost certainly look in your direction. Constancy is the hallmark of your nature and unfaithfulness would go right against the grain. You might sometimes be a little too trusting.

Venus in Aquarius

This location of Venus offers a fondness for travel and a desire to try out something new at every possible opportunity. You are extremely easy to get along with and tend to have many friends from varied backgrounds, classes and inclinations. You like to live a distinct sort of life and gain a great deal from moving about, both in a career sense and with regard to your home. It is not out of the question that you could form a romantic attachment to someone who comes from far away or be attracted to a person of a distinctly artistic and original nature. What you cannot stand is jealousy, for you have friends of both sexes and would want to keep things that way.

Venus in Pisces

The first thing people tend to notice about you is your wonderful, warm smile. Being very charitable by nature you will do anything to help others, even if you don't know them well. Much of your life may be spent sorting out situations for other people, but it is very important to feel that you are living for yourself too. In the main, you remain cheerful, and tend to be quite attractive to members of the opposite sex. Where romantic attachments are concerned, you could be drawn to people who are significantly older or younger than yourself or to someone with a unique career or point of view. It might be best for you to avoid marrying whilst you are still very young.

HOW THE DIAGRAMS WORK

Through the picture diagrams in the Astral Diary I want to help you to plot your year. With them you can see where the positive and negative aspects will be found in each month. To make the most of them, all you have to do is remember where and when!

Let me show you how they work ...

THE MONTH AT A GLANCE

Just as there are twelve separate zodiac signs, so astrologers believe that each sign has twelve separate aspects to life. Each of the twelve segments relates to a different personal aspect. I list them all every month so that their meanings are always clear.

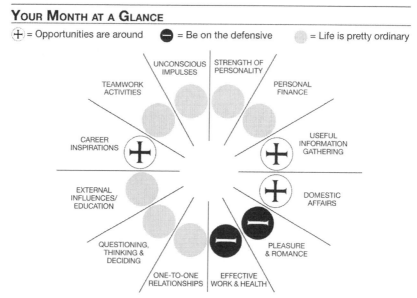

YOUR MONTH AT A GLANCE

⊕ = Opportunities are around   ⚊ = Be on the defensive   ⚬ = Life is pretty ordinary

I have designed this chart to show you how and when these twelve different aspects are being influenced throughout the year. When there is a shaded circle, nothing out of the ordinary is to be expected. However, when a circle turns white with a plus sign, the influence is positive. Where the circle is black with a minus sign, it is a negative.

YOUR ENERGY RHYTHM CHART

Below is a picture diagram in which I link your zodiac group to the rhythm of the Moon. In doing this I have calculated when you will be gaining strength from its influence and equally when you may be weakened by it.

If you think of yourself as being like the tides of the ocean then you may understand how your own energies must also rise and fall. And if you understand how it works and when it is working, then you can better organise your activities to achieve more and get things done more easily.

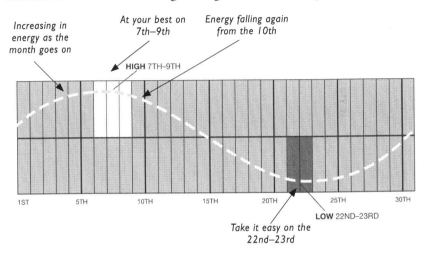

THE KEY DAYS

Some of the entries are in **bold**, which indicates the working of astrological cycles in your life. Look out for them each week as they are the best days to take action or make decisions. The daily text tells you which area of your life to focus on.

MERCURY RETROGRADE

The Mercury symbol (☿) indicates that Mercury is retrograde on that day. Since Mercury governs communication, the fact that it appears to be moving backwards when viewed from the Earth at this time should warn you that your communication skills are not likely to be at their best and you could expect some setbacks.

CANCER: YOUR YEAR IN BRIEF

Almost from the very start of the year, it should be obvious that you are keen to get on with things and that you will be putting behind you some of the less favourable aspects of 2014. In January and February, you could be going through a time of retrenchment. You will be anxious to make progress at work and may have slightly less time for relatives and friends as a result. Confidence is especially high as the month of February comes to an end.

At the beginning of spring, your mind is apt to turn towards personal associations in life. Don't be too quick to let go of something important in terms of relationships and try to spend time with those who know you the best. It would be best to avoid too much speculation during March and April, though there are significant successes of a non-monetary type. April will probably be especially good in terms of your intellect and the way it functions.

May and June are good for consolidating your general position and for reaping some financial rewards, possibly as a result of efforts you have put into life previously. With the warmer weather and the summer comes an urge to be on the move and a continuation of the restlessness that keeps returning this year. You should be able to get others to follow your lead when it matters the most.

With July comes a whole string of new incentives, together with a definite upward turn in the quality of your personal life. The summer will be especially good for romance and some Crabs will be forming significant new attachments at this time. August finds you anxious to travel, not just on holiday but also for other reasons. A whole series of positive events may bring happiness to the family around this time.

September and October could be slightly quieter and you won't have quite the level of energy that was the case in the high summer. This doesn't really matter, because you are working towards your objectives in a different and more considered way. People like you and it really shows. Journeys that you planned earlier in the year could be enjoyable, even if they are only short trips.

The last two months of the year are likely to be a whirl of activity and offer you new starts, sporting activities and better creative potential. Your thoughts about Christmas are turned into hard-and-fast reality and you will work hard to offer everyone you encounter a good time. There is likely to be a good deal of nostalgia around, but that is quite normal for the Crab. The very end of the year could be marked with ambitious new plans and a strong sense of co-operation.

January

2015

Your Month at a Glance

$+$ = Opportunities are around   ⬤ = Be on the defensive   = Life is pretty ordinary

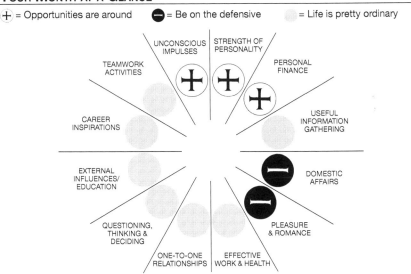

UNCONSCIOUS IMPULSES

STRENGTH OF PERSONALITY

TEAMWORK ACTIVITIES

PERSONAL FINANCE

CAREER INSPIRATIONS

USEFUL INFORMATION GATHERING

EXTERNAL INFLUENCES/ EDUCATION

DOMESTIC AFFAIRS

QUESTIONING, THINKING & DECIDING

PLEASURE & ROMANCE

ONE-TO-ONE RELATIONSHIPS

EFFECTIVE WORK & HEALTH

January Highs and Lows

Here I show you how the rhythms of the Moon will affect you this month. Like the tide, your energies and abilities will rise and fall with its pattern. When it is above the centre line, go for it, when it is below, you should be resting.

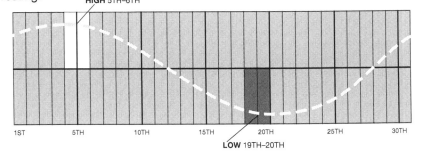

HIGH 5TH–6TH

1ST   5TH   10TH   15TH   20TH   25TH   30TH

LOW 19TH–20TH

45

1 THURSDAY
Moon Age Day 11   Moon Sign Taurus

You are going to have to tell a few white lies if you really want to get your own way at the start of the year. This sort of behaviour doesn't come at all easy to you, so take advantage of the planetary trends highlighting communication. Anything really old or distinctly curious is apt to appeal to you during the remainder of this week.

2 FRIDAY
Moon Age Day 12   Moon Sign Gemini

Conserve some of your energy because the social trends are getting better and better. If you wear yourself out during the day, you won't have either the drive or the initiative to make the most of what the evening has to offer. Whatever the weather, it's important to get plenty of fresh air now.

3 SATURDAY
Moon Age Day 13   Moon Sign Gemini

If you are a weekend worker, keep up the pressure in professional matters. If you're not, find ways to enjoy yourself. Most Cancer subjects like to keep busy and with creative potential good at the moment, it isn't out of the question that you will be decorating your home or helping with projects at a friend's house.

4 SUNDAY
Moon Age Day 14   Moon Sign Gemini

Little unexpected gains are there for the taking. You won't become a millionaire today, but if you keep your wits about you there is a possibility you could take the first step. You are never anyone's fool, but at the moment your perceptions are razor sharp. Use strong intuition when assessing others.

5 MONDAY
Moon Age Day 15   Moon Sign Cancer

The Moon is in your zodiac sign, bringing the lunar high, that time during each month when you are emotionally and physically motivated. Anything you decide to do today is undertaken with a great deal of enthusiasm and plenty of determination. What is more, you have Lady Luck on your side.

6 TUESDAY
Moon Age Day 16   Moon Sign Cancer

Keep up the effort. Even things you have had great difficulty doing in the past come that much easier today. If you have to enlist the help and support of friends or colleagues, simply turn on the charm. It's doubtful that anyone could turn down a reasonable request from your direction at present.

7 WEDNESDAY
Moon Age Day 17 Moon Sign Leo

You could be very motivated today, especially during the afternoon and evening. If you are feeling a surge of wanderlust, now is the time to exploit that fact by taking a journey. Don't be too quick to judge younger family members, no matter how they seem to be behaving.

8 THURSDAY
Moon Age Day 18 Moon Sign Leo

Stay away from get-rich-quick schemes. Your intuition tells you that there is a good chance you will get your fingers burned, so why take the risk? A new hobby could be up your street at the moment, especially if it is one that has a physical dimension.

9 FRIDAY
Moon Age Day 19 Moon Sign Virgo

Your personality profile currently shows that you are slightly more difficult to fathom than is likely to have been the case earlier in the month. Be as open as you can and make it plain to people that you are not worrying about anything. When the Crab withdraws, it is a problematic zodiac sign to understand.

10 SATURDAY
Moon Age Day 20 Moon Sign Virgo

The weekend sees a change of pace, or at least an alteration in the way you view your life. Slower and steadier now, you may decide that you need to spend more time in the bosom of your family. Failing this, you could be looking up friends you haven't seen for quite a while.

11 SUNDAY
Moon Age Day 21 Moon Sign Virgo

There are times when maximum effort is necessary and other periods when you should take things slowly and steadily. Your deeper thought processes are working really well now, so mull situations over carefully. If necessary, enlist the direct intervention of a friend.

12 MONDAY
Moon Age Day 22 Moon Sign Libra

Stick to paths you understand for the moment, but prepare yourself for an imminent major push. This might seem an uneventful sort of day, but it is the things that are happening below the surface that you should be watching carefully. Close personal ties should be working well for you now.

13 TUESDAY
Moon Age Day 23 Moon Sign Libra

Today should prove to be eventful and especially good in social matters. You are mixing freely with all sorts of individuals, even some you haven't cared for all that much previously. Some Crabs will be very hobby minded just now and the creative spark is strong.

14 WEDNESDAY
Moon Age Day 24 Moon Sign Scorpio

Beware of planetary trends that make you more absentminded than would normally be the case and make this a day to write some lists. You will proceed normally, just as long as you review matters early in the day and don't forget anything important. Family gatherings are distinctly possible at present.

15 THURSDAY
Moon Age Day 25 Moon Sign Scorpio

There probably won't be a great deal of spare time today. Life is busy and you feel a good deal of pressure being placed upon your shoulders. You can deal with this so much better if you are prepared. What you really need to avoid is being surprised by issues you don't understand.

16 FRIDAY
Moon Age Day 26 Moon Sign Scorpio

Dealings with others show up your real diplomatic skills today. Although you might not be the most confident of people in the world when you begin to talk, as time wears on you grow more comfortable. People are listening to you with great attention and take as much from your silences as from your words.

17 SATURDAY
Moon Age Day 27 Moon Sign Sagittarius

There are few tasks that appear to be beyond you at this time. Pitch in and have a go, because you can show a disbelieving world exactly what you are capable of achieving. Confidence is everything and you make friends and influence people today simply by being your own, cheerful self.

18 SUNDAY
Moon Age Day 28 Moon Sign Sagittarius

Sunday should bring a definite boost to your social life and might find you mixing more freely with the sort of people you may sometimes avoid. Romance is on the cards for young or young-at-heart Cancer subjects, with compliments coming to all Crabs, sometimes from unexpected directions.

19 MONDAY
Moon Age Day 29   Moon Sign Capricorn

This will be a quieter day and one that works better with contemplation, instead of action. Do your best to take life steadily, watching from the banks as the river of life flows by. It might seem rather unproductive, but at the end of the day you function better when you have time to think.

20 TUESDAY
Moon Age Day 0   Moon Sign Capricorn

Things are still likely to be slow, but don't worry because these trends certainly won't last long. Confidence is not especially high, that is unless you enlist the support of people you really know well and trust. Spend some time with family members and find the right words to tell them how much you care.

21 WEDNESDAY
Moon Age Day 1   Moon Sign Aquarius

Prepare to make the most of your social life. Although you might not be tying yourself down too much with romantic attachments, across the board you are getting on with people extremely well. However, there are signs that there could be disappointments at work or in practical matters.

22 THURSDAY ☿
Moon Age Day 2   Moon Sign Aquarius

Mental and cultural pursuits can all be uplifting today. It's time to stretch your mind, and there won't be any lack of people willing to participate. You would do well in any sort of quiz now, or when put to the test at work. Your powers of recall are good and you are more than willing to participate.

23 FRIDAY ☿
Moon Age Day 3   Moon Sign Pisces

There may be the odd challenge to deal with today, perhaps as a result of the fact that you can't agree with everyone. Some people appear determined to be difficult. As a rule you would simply shrug your shoulders and accept the situation, but not today, it appears.

24 SATURDAY ☿
Moon Age Day 4   Moon Sign Pisces

You need encouragement, particularly from your partner. Unfortunately, this may not be forthcoming and so you will have to soldier on alone for a good deal of the day. This is not a state of affairs that is likely to last long, so you don't need to set too much store by what is, after all, a very temporary period.

25 SUNDAY ☿

Moon Age Day 5 Moon Sign Aries

You may have to dig deep in order to get to the roots of an emotional matter today, not particularly one that directly concerns you, but rather on behalf of someone else. It is clear that you are being singled out to lend a listening ear – a state of affairs that might not prove to be all that comfortable.

26 MONDAY ☿

Moon Age Day 6 Moon Sign Aries

Make the most of influences that point towards satisfying results at work. Not only could you receive a good deal more in the way of support from colleagues, but you could also find that circumstances generally seem to be bending to your will. It could appear that fate is on your side in a number of different ways.

27 TUESDAY ☿

Moon Age Day 7 Moon Sign Taurus

You enjoy exploring the big, wide world today. Don't stay behind closed doors, but enjoy what astrological Crabs love, which is to explore fresh fields and pastures new. True, the weather won't be too good yet, but you can always wrap up warm. Once you are back behind your own door, you will feel enlivened by your experiences.

28 WEDNESDAY ☿

Moon Age Day 8 Moon Sign Taurus

Socially speaking, things are getting better and better, whilst at the same time coming to terms with your opposite is easier, too. Shining in public is really quite simple for you today. Getting tasks out of the way early in the day allows you more and more time to do those things that appeal the most.

29 THURSDAY ☿

Moon Age Day 9 Moon Sign Gemini

Though your powers of persuasion are good at present, there are some people who will not come round to your point of view, no matter what you say to them. Accept this and don't spend too much time trying to move mountains. There are other people to meet and alternative ways to spend your time.

30 FRIDAY ☿

Moon Age Day 10 Moon Sign Gemini

Creative potential is good, especially around the home. You might have less incentive right now to go travelling, though you would benefit from a shopping spree of some sort. If you are being recommended to fulfil some sort of social role in your neighbourhood, it is genuinely because people trust you.

31 SATURDAY ☿ *Moon Age Day 11 Moon Sign Gemini*

Financial complexity could be surrounding you at this time. You need to keep a careful eye on how much you are spending. Luxury goods are allowed, of course, but probably not many. What counts the most right now is that you read any small print carefully or, better still, leave dealing with documents for another time.

February

2015

YOUR MONTH AT A GLANCE

⊕ = Opportunities are around   ⊖ = Be on the defensive   ⬤ = Life is pretty ordinary

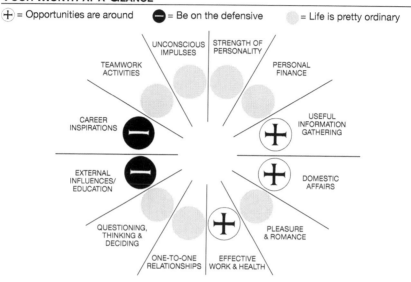

- UNCONSCIOUS IMPULSES
- STRENGTH OF PERSONALITY
- TEAMWORK ACTIVITIES
- PERSONAL FINANCE
- CAREER INSPIRATIONS ⊖
- USEFUL INFORMATION GATHERING ⊕
- EXTERNAL INFLUENCES/ EDUCATION ⊖
- DOMESTIC AFFAIRS ⊕
- QUESTIONING, THINKING & DECIDING
- PLEASURE & ROMANCE
- ONE-TO-ONE RELATIONSHIPS
- EFFECTIVE WORK & HEALTH ⊕

FEBRUARY HIGHS AND LOWS

Here I show you how the rhythms of the Moon will affect you this month. Like the tide, your energies and abilities will rise and fall with its pattern. When it is above the centre line, go for it, when it is below, you should be resting.

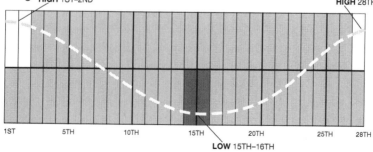

HIGH 1ST–2ND   HIGH 28TH

1ST   5TH   10TH   15TH   20TH   25TH   28TH

LOW 15TH–16TH

1 SUNDAY *Moon Age Day 12 Moon Sign Cancer*

The lunar high finds you in good sprits and more than anxious to do almost anything you can to get ahead. The Crab is a builder at the moment, whether it is in relationships or out there in the business world. It becomes plain today that you have more to give than you have been offering so far this year.

2 MONDAY *Moon Age Day 13 Moon Sign Cancer*

The positive trends continue and Lady Luck pays a potentially important visit to your life. Ignore restraints and push through obstacles. There are plenty of new incentives about, the difference now being that you notice them. Concern for friends who find themselves in a dilemma turns to practical assistance.

3 TUESDAY *Moon Age Day 14 Moon Sign Leo*

Something inside you is screaming that you should be putting your point of view forward more strongly, and that is certainly the case at work. If you are looking for a job at the moment, today could be a good time to make further enquiries. There might not be much excitement about, but there is potential gain.

4 WEDNESDAY ☿ *Moon Age Day 15 Moon Sign Leo*

That wit is still showing strongly. You have a great ability to make almost anyone laugh today and if there is something you have to complain about, you do so with humour. Rules and regulations are inclined to get on your nerves right now, unless you decide to ignore them altogether.

5 THURSDAY ☿ *Moon Age Day 16 Moon Sign Leo*

You have an amazing ability to go straight to the heart of just about any matter now. It would be great if you could decide to take today off work, because you are also feeling somewhat hemmed in by responsibility and general circumstances. What you seem to need most of all now is a temporary change of scenery.

6 FRIDAY ☿ *Moon Age Day 17 Moon Sign Virgo*

Standing up for your rights and for those of the people you care for seems to be very important at present, but so is making sure you have something to complain about before you get cracking. Checking details is important in every sphere of your life today and particularly in travel arrangements.

7 SATURDAY ☿ *Moon Age Day 18 Moon Sign Virgo*

Anything to do with modern technology not only attracts you at the moment, but also shows how your mind tends to work. You can be more logical than a Vulcan and arrive at some startling conclusions this weekend as a result. Try to get away from too many family-based domestic routines.

8 SUNDAY ☿ *Moon Age Day 19 Moon Sign Libra*

If there is something you don't like today, ignore it. This isn't usually the sort of advice that would be offered to you, but it is highly likely that you are getting yourself into a state about nothing. Clear your head by taking a long walk and perhaps give some thought to long-term changes in your career.

9 MONDAY ☿ *Moon Age Day 20 Moon Sign Libra*

You are well ahead of the competition in some respects, even though it may look as if others are making more progress than you are. What is required is a little patience and confidence in your own past decisions. There are times during this part of the week when it is vital for you to keep your nerve.

10 TUESDAY ☿ *Moon Age Day 21 Moon Sign Libra*

You should be getting on fine in a general sense, despite the fact that you don't have quite the level of self-belief that you deserve. Constant attention to detail could get on your nerves right now, which is why a change of job would be as good as a rest. A general overview of life works well, if you can manage it.

11 WEDNESDAY ☿ *Moon Age Day 22 Moon Sign Scorpio*

Take advantage of your growing confidence in your own vision of the future. You may be less inclined to look back to past situations, but that cannot be said for everyone around you, though your persuasive skills could make all the difference. Believe and you can have almost anything now.

12 THURSDAY ☿ *Moon Age Day 23 Moon Sign Scorpio*

There are signs that you are definitely working at your best in an intellectual sense. You would be especially good at any sort of competitions now and would positively devour IQ tests. Maybe you can look at yourself and really understand the many different levels on which your versatile mind functions.

13 FRIDAY ☿ *Moon Age Day 24   Moon Sign Sagittarius*

The end of the working week for many Crabs means putting in that extra bit of effort that is going to prove so worthwhile next week. By the evening, you will be ready to party and that might mean getting together with friends. Your sparkling personality is on display and marks you out for extra attention.

14 SATURDAY *Moon Age Day 25   Moon Sign Sagittarius*

Things may not be happening quite the way you intended, but that doesn't mean they work against your best interests. Keep a sense of proportion when dealing with romantic matters and don't be surprised if you turn someone's head, even without trying. The charisma of the Crab is now evident.

15 SUNDAY *Moon Age Day 26   Moon Sign Capricorn*

If you're not feeling at your best today, or at least not returning the number of successes you might wish, you can blame the lunar low, though its presence in your life does at least give you the chance to take a break. Avoid family disputes, or at least try to sort them out quickly.

16 MONDAY *Moon Age Day 27   Moon Sign Capricorn*

You could be somewhat forgetful today and inclined to miss out on one or two things as a result. Don't be too quick to take on extra responsibilities and be willing to wait for successes, which are slow in maturing. Confidence gradually begins to return, though even tomorrow could start slowly.

17 TUESDAY *Moon Age Day 28   Moon Sign Aquarius*

Professional tasks are likely to keep you rather busy at the moment and there may not be quite as much time as you would wish for having fun. However, by the evening there may be some hours to please yourself, which you may choose to spend in the company of family members, rather than friends.

18 WEDNESDAY *Moon Age Day 29   Moon Sign Aquarius*

You can keep up a varied and interesting social life today, which is probably just as well since professional progress appears to be rather limited. Not everyone is your friend right now, though it is hard to see what you have done to create the situation. Some people are simply awkward!

19 THURSDAY
Moon Age Day 0 Moon Sign Pisces

Do avoid forcing your ideas on relatives and friends. By all means use a degree of persuasion, but in the end, you must allow people to do things in their own way. Chances are that when you turn on the charm, you are likely to get your own way in any case. All it takes is that Cancer tact.

20 FRIDAY
Moon Age Day 1 Moon Sign Pisces

Outdoor pursuits could be of particular appeal at present. Home-loving and quiet Cancer can still be quite competitive, and a win will boost your ego no end. If you are tired of following the same old routines, now is the time to break out and to begin something new and even revolutionary.

21 SATURDAY
Moon Age Day 2 Moon Sign Aries

This is a time for emphasising your practical skills and for showing any Doubting Thomas that you know what you are doing. Work life is highlighted now, so don't pass up the chance to go for any promotion that comes your way. For those of you who are simply determined to relax on a Saturday, there could be some luxury in store.

22 SUNDAY
Moon Age Day 3 Moon Sign Aries

A lengthy discussion could help you to sort out problems that have been around for a while. Your powers of communication appear to be excellent at the moment, so why not make use of them? Romance is a possibility for many Cancer subjects at this time, even if you may not be expecting it.

23 MONDAY
Moon Age Day 4 Moon Sign Aries

There are lots of interesting ideas in the air. All you need to do is to quantify them and to work out how best to make them work. If you get the chance of a break from routine and maybe even a journey today, you should grab it with both hands. Don't leave a friend out in the cold with a problem you can easily solve.

24 TUESDAY
Moon Age Day 5 Moon Sign Taurus

You can now get to the very heart of practical matters and should be able to do that one important thing that can make all the difference in the end. Confidence is what it takes to make this Tuesday special. Even if it isn't present, you can pretend. You will be surprised at how convincing you can be.

25 WEDNESDAY
Moon Age Day 6 Moon Sign Taurus

Make sure you are not deceiving yourself when it comes to personal and even intimate decisions at present. It is possible that you need another point of view and there are people around who can deliver. A little embarrassment is nothing if you feel very much better in the end.

26 THURSDAY
Moon Age Day 7 Moon Sign Gemini

This could prove to be rather routine sort of day, but might be none the worse for that. What it means is that you can get through a great many jobs, and still feel fresh enough later to find ways and means of enjoying yourself. What you can do right now is relax while you work, an enviable state of affairs.

27 FRIDAY
Moon Age Day 8 Moon Sign Gemini

Today ought to be favourable for progress of a very specific type. This is not a time when you will be trying to do a thousand different jobs at once, but if your mind is focused, almost anything becomes possible. Not everything turns out exactly as you would wish, but there are occasions when life knows best.

28 SATURDAY
Moon Age Day 9 Moon Sign Cancer

Now the Moon is firmly settled in your zodiac sign and the time comes for having fun. Most of your aims and objectives are reasonable and you can find a higher degree of good luck coming your way. Confidence is not lacking and you can afford some limited speculation during today and tomorrow.

March
2015

Your Month at a Glance

⊕ = Opportunities are around   ⊖ = Be on the defensive   ○ = Life is pretty ordinary

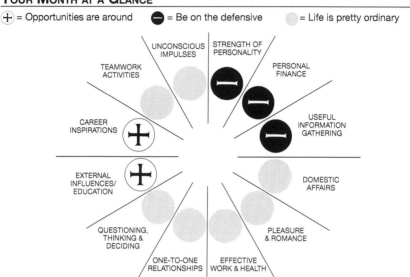

March Highs and Lows

Here I show you how the rhythms of the Moon will affect you this month. Like the tide, your energies and abilities will rise and fall with its pattern. When it is above the centre line, go for it, when it is below, you should be resting.

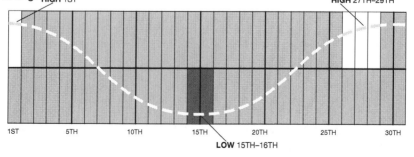

1 SUNDAY
Moon Age Day 10 Moon Sign Cancer

If you don't get everything you want today, it certainly isn't through a lack of application. You can make most situations your own and influence greatly the way other people are thinking. Turn on the charm in the way you are doing at the moment and the world is your oyster.

2 MONDAY
Moon Age Day 11 Moon Sign Leo

This is potentially a time of small but regular increases where finances are concerned. Concentrate your effort in places and situations you know and understand. You show a strong willingness to help others, especially friends you recognise to be going through a hard time at the moment.

3 TUESDAY
Moon Age Day 12 Moon Sign Leo

There could be a love interest on the horizon for the Crab, particularly those of you who have been looking for that very special romance. Don't be too quick to jump to conclusions regarding material matters and if you are in any doubt whatsoever, opt for a patient attitude and bide your time.

4 WEDNESDAY
Moon Age Day 13 Moon Sign Leo

There is a chance you could get carried away with matters that don't concern you today. Retain your energy for really important tasks. Although you have plenty of get up and go right now, it is easily dissipated. It's quality, rather than quantity that could bring the rewards.

5 THURSDAY
Moon Age Day 14 Moon Sign Virgo

The time is right for attracting new people into your life. Although there is a definite shy side to your nature, it doesn't show all that much at present. Most Cancerians will be young at heart, no matter what their age might be. Go for fun, because that's the most important factor now.

6 FRIDAY
Moon Age Day 15 Moon Sign Virgo

Mundane and domestic matters can be trying, which is why you are looking for diversity in your day. Confidence remains generally high, though there are people around who would change that situation if they could. Watch out for someone who wants to throw a spanner in the works.

7 SATURDAY
Moon Age Day 16 Moon Sign Libra

It could be a good idea to vary your routines just as much as possible this weekend, without planning anything too much. If you remain flexible, all sorts of possibilities could open up you. You might even find that people you haven't seen for some time could turn up on your doorstep.

8 SUNDAY
Moon Age Day 17 Moon Sign Libra

You should now be registering a genuinely lighthearted period, during which you find the answers you need almost without trying. If you do come up against the odd problem today, there is likely to be someone around who will solve it for you. The difference now is that you are not too shy or retiring to ask.

9 MONDAY
Moon Age Day 18 Moon Sign Libra

There are positive trends associated with all areas of your life at the moment, though the main accent has to be on practical and professional matters. If you have had some sort of idea in your head, possibly for earning more money, you really should take it out of the cupboard and look at it more closely now.

10 TUESDAY
Moon Age Day 19 Moon Sign Scorpio

Differences of opinion in your vicinity don't really have to have a bearing on the way you behave, especially if you refuse to take a stance. The fact that you won't get involved might slightly annoy others, but in the end they will respect you more for remaining neutral. You can then play the honest broker.

11 WEDNESDAY
Moon Age Day 20 Moon Sign Scorpio

There is much to captivate your interest now, socially and romantically. It is possible that you are well ahead in your work, which ought to leave time for simply enjoying yourself. Consolidation is one of the most important factors for the Crab now, in spite of a spontaneous attitude.

12 THURSDAY
Moon Age Day 21 Moon Sign Sagittarius

Nothing ventured, nothing gained should be your adage now. Yours is not a zodiac sign that is used to taking too many chances, but if you don't do so now, you could be the loser. If you have any doubts, seek out the help and advice of a good friend who can point you in the right direction.

13 FRIDAY
Moon Age Day 22   Moon Sign Sagittarius

Intimate concerns and domestic situations seem to be your most important priorities around now. At what is probably the end of a working week, you might not be all that happy with the general progress you have made, but you have probably done much better overall than you realise.

14 SATURDAY
Moon Age Day 23   Moon Sign Sagittarius

There are signs that certain people can sorely test your patience today, especially at work. For this reason alone, the focus of life needs to be pushed towards home, family and friendship today. Assume for now that work is something you have to do, whereas your greatest pleasures lie temporarily elsewhere.

15 SUNDAY
Moon Age Day 24   Moon Sign Capricorn

You might be at your most energetic at the moment, but you are in a good position to weigh up situations. Try not to have to make too many important decisions; leaving this until Tuesday, if you can. Relax and let others take some of the strain for the moment.

16 MONDAY
Moon Age Day 25   Moon Sign Capricorn

Enthusiasm is in short supply. You can do much better if you get some support and encouragement, particularly from your partner. Remember that anything you don't get done today will probably be achieved much easier later. Finding friends who are willing to spend time with you should be easy.

17 TUESDAY
Moon Age Day 26   Moon Sign Aquarius

Don't be surprised if your personal finances feel rather less secure at present than you might have hoped. It shouldn't be too difficult to rein in your spending somewhat. In any case, the most important things in life at the moment tend to come free of charge.

18 WEDNESDAY
Moon Age Day 27   Moon Sign Aquarius

Don't be afraid to make snap decisions, if that is what it takes to get on well in life. Confidence may not be quite as high as you would wish in domestic or personal matters, but this is a temporary phenomenon and won't be an issue later. Friends can be very supportive over financial issues.

19 THURSDAY
Moon Age Day 28 Moon Sign Pisces

Home comforts have a special appeal now, probably because you are tending to shy away from the wider world to a certain extent. This isn't so unusual. Your zodiac sign is often committed to the place where you feel most secure. Paradoxically, you might also feel the need to travel around this time.

20 FRIDAY
Moon Age Day 0 Moon Sign Pisces

There is certainly no doubting your loyalty at present, or your commitment to people who have looked after you in the past. Finding time to do what pleases you will be quite difficult today, but since you are probably on the go from morning until night, this won't occur to you until later.

21 SATURDAY
Moon Age Day 1 Moon Sign Aries

Take advantages of planetary trends highlighting communication and look out for some news that could liven things up no end. You are in the mood for excitement and will want to help others have a good time as well. Confidence is generally high and you show a great desire to ring the changes in one way or another, specifically with regard to travel.

22 SUNDAY
Moon Age Day 2 Moon Sign Aries

There is much to be said for jumping at opportunities to break with routines and to spend at least part of the Sunday doing something different. You can't be on the go all the time, and wouldn't want to be, but a change is as good as a rest. Try a shopping trip, or maybe an out-of-season trip to the coast or country.

23 MONDAY
Moon Age Day 3 Moon Sign Taurus

This is not a good time to be involved in conflict with either colleagues or friends. You are going to get on much better if you create a harmonious atmosphere, though you don't have to subjugate your own wishes to do so. It is possible to be diplomatic but firm, something that most people will respect.

24 TUESDAY
Moon Age Day 4 Moon Sign Taurus

Look out for your ego today. If you take anything great on, you could be in for a shock. Keep life light and even, and that way you won't be disappointed. On the personal front, you can expect more attention to be coming your way any time now, leading to a fairly interesting time, at least for some.

25 WEDNESDAY
Moon Age Day 5 Moon Sign Gemini

This is a great time to be forging ahead with new plans. The Sun is now in your solar tenth house, giving more grit and determination. This is also a good time for romance, particularly for young or young-at-heart Cancer subjects. Those of you with well-established relationships may experience more passion.

26 THURSDAY
Moon Age Day 6 Moon Sign Gemini

Some challenges occur on a practical level, but you deal with them easily enough. You may be surprised at your own competence, even with matters about which you are not generally sure. In terms of practical efforts, once you have made up your mind to a particular course of action, it would be best to stick to it.

27 FRIDAY
Moon Age Day 7 Moon Sign Cancer

With your high spirits and energy soaring from the start of the day, it appears that you can achieve a great deal now. With any venture, it would be sensible to strike whilst the iron is hot. It doesn't really matter in which direction you choose to turn your energies today, because success is your middle name.

28 SATURDAY
Moon Age Day 8 Moon Sign Cancer

This is another day that appears to be geared, fundamentally, towards personal success. You could be chattier than usual and willing to put your point of view to just about anyone who is willing to listen. This means employers, too, and the impression you make will not be wasted.

29 SUNDAY
Moon Age Day 9 Moon Sign Cancer

Getting your own way with just about anyone should be possible at present, not that you have to force any issue. Your natural good nature and pleasant ways will be enough. If you have any enemies, you can certainly take the wind out of their sails today. Impressing the world is not at all difficult.

30 MONDAY
Moon Age Day 10 Moon Sign Leo

Beware of controversy and mixing with the wrong people today. You could find yourself being tarred with altogether the wrong brush and all because you are taking invalid advice. Use your own common sense and speak with your own voice. That way, nobody will get the wrong idea.

31 TUESDAY
Moon Age Day 11   Moon Sign Leo

This is a favourable time for social outings and any form of personal contact with people you love. It could be possible to shift some of a forthcoming workload today, leaving you with more time to please yourself for a while.

April
2015

Your Month at a Glance

$\oplus$ = Opportunities are around $\ominus$ = Be on the defensive $\bigcirc$ = Life is pretty ordinary

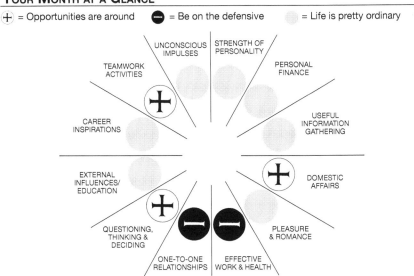

UNCONSCIOUS IMPULSES

STRENGTH OF PERSONALITY

TEAMWORK ACTIVITIES

PERSONAL FINANCE

CAREER INSPIRATIONS

USEFUL INFORMATION GATHERING

EXTERNAL INFLUENCES/ EDUCATION

DOMESTIC AFFAIRS

QUESTIONING, THINKING & DECIDING

PLEASURE & ROMANCE

ONE-TO-ONE RELATIONSHIPS

EFFECTIVE WORK & HEALTH

April Highs and Lows

Here I show you how the rhythms of the Moon will affect you this month. Like the tide, your energies and abilities will rise and fall with its pattern. When it is above the centre line, go for it, when it is below, you should be resting.

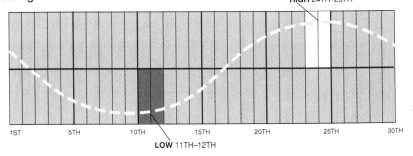

HIGH 24TH–25TH

1ST   5TH   10TH   15TH   20TH   25TH   30TH

LOW 11TH–12TH

1 WEDNESDAY
Moon Age Day 12 Moon Sign Virgo

A professional issue could cause a rather tense atmosphere today, unless you take it by the scruff of the neck and deal with it immediately. You need to be very direct in all your dealings right now, because hedging your bets doesn't work. Friends display a lack of confidence in you, which could be disquieting.

2 THURSDAY
Moon Age Day 13 Moon Sign Virgo

There is scope today for you to enjoy being the centre of attention wherever you go. It would be a shame to waste this opportunity simply because this was nothing more than a routine day. Put yourself out to make sure there are social possibilities after work.

3 FRIDAY
Moon Age Day 14 Moon Sign Virgo

You know the value of self-reliance and can easily go your own way. This is particularly true today. Your nature is rock solid, causing others to have a deep and abiding confidence in your decision. If this places an extra burden on you, you don't appear to recognise it.

4 SATURDAY
Moon Age Day 15 Moon Sign Libra

This is a good day to be around the people you care for the most. Although you have been a distinctly social person on quite a few occasions recently, in the main you are happiest when you understand your surroundings and the people within it. One or two friends prove to be positively inspiring.

5 SUNDAY
Moon Age Day 16 Moon Sign Libra

Having fun is likely to be your number one priority this Sunday. Although this is somewhat difficult in the midst of a busy life, make the most of opportunities to mix business with pleasure and to enjoy them both. Look out for people who haven't been around recently and take the chance to have a chat.

6 MONDAY
Moon Age Day 17 Moon Sign Scorpio

Professional issues are now taken in your stride, proving once again how reliable you are, even when under some small stress. You can't expect everyone to agree with your point of view at the moment, but in the end you will invariably turn out to be right. People should listen to the Crab more than they do!

7 TUESDAY
Moon Age Day 18 Moon Sign Scorpio

Be prepared for some minor mishaps today, but don't worry: most of them can be viewed in a humorous way. It is hard to take anything particularly seriously now and you really want to have fun. The practical joker within you now shows out, and this facet of your nature continues in the days ahead.

8 WEDNESDAY
Moon Age Day 19 Moon Sign Scorpio

Today is partly about coming to terms with a personal issue. Be confident in your dealings with others and don't give anyone the impression that you are not steady in your decision-making. Friends should prove to be especially helpful at the moment and genuinely want to lend a hand.

9 THURSDAY
Moon Age Day 20 Moon Sign Sagittarius

The time is right for focusing on the practical aspects of life. You can discover a number of new ways to get ahead with your work and should also be enjoying the cut and thrust of an active life that could involve colleagues. Family matters might have to be left on the backburner for a short while.

10 FRIDAY
Moon Age Day 21 Moon Sign Sagittarius

A relationship might give you pause for thought, as your partner behaves in a most unlikely manner. Don't spend too much time worrying today. The busier you are, the more things will improve. Make long-term plans that involve finances as quickly as you can and make sure you stick to your word at this time.

11 SATURDAY
Moon Age Day 22 Moon Sign Capricorn

Avoid pushing yourself too hard today. The lunar low is around and you should be far enough ahead in a general sense not to have to rush. Take time out to look, think and plan. Personal attachments should be sound and capable of offering a warm glow when you need it the most.

12 SUNDAY
Moon Age Day 23 Moon Sign Capricorn

Although today appears to mark something of a low point for your fortunes, it is actually nothing of the sort. Instead of trying to push ahead against the odds, it would be sensible now to simply go with the flow, accepting that by tomorrow almost anything can look completely different.

13 MONDAY
Moon Age Day 24 Moon Sign Aquarius

Practical issues and general run-of-the-mill situations are likely to take up much of your time today. Although you are likely to get plenty done, this probably could not be considered a particularly successful day. Creative potential is especially good now and needs to be utilised in some way.

14 TUESDAY
Moon Age Day 25 Moon Sign Aquarius

A financial issue is apt to prove somewhat complicated, leading you to seek the advice of someone who is more in the know than you are. Don't avoid discussions, simply because you are not in a chatty frame of mind. Things need sorting out and you won't manage that without talking.

15 WEDNESDAY
Moon Age Day 26 Moon Sign Pisces

Suddenly there is a very strong emphasis on fun and it is possible that you find it difficult to take certain matters seriously. You might have to pretend that you do, though only for the sake of those around you. Give yourself a genuine pat on the back for a recent success that is likely to lead to others.

16 THURSDAY
Moon Age Day 27 Moon Sign Pisces

You could be at serious loggerheads with someone over a personal matter. Even if it means disagreeing, it would probably be better to talk things through, rather than to keep silent on the issue. Harbouring resentments isn't good for anyone, but especially not for sensitive Cancer types.

17 FRIDAY
Moon Age Day 28 Moon Sign Aries

You can get a great deal from professional matters today, a period that is excellent for working Crabs. Don't be inclined to hold back, just because someone thinks they know better than you do. Their judgement is probably subjective and, since you are a deep thinker, you may have the intellectual and moral high ground.

18 SATURDAY
Moon Age Day 29 Moon Sign Aries

There is a chance that a friend could turn out to be something of a letdown today. This is part of life. You are loyal beyond belief and tend to expect everyone to be the same. Unfortunately, this is not the case. If you don't entertain such unreasonable expectations of the world at large, you are less likely to be disappointed.

19 SUNDAY
Moon Age Day 0   Moon Sign Taurus

You can expect a fairly successful sort of Sunday if you keep on the move. This is not going to be the sort of day to hide your light under a bushel. Keep an open mind about social possibilities and enjoy what life has to offer in terms of romantic interludes.

20 MONDAY
Moon Age Day 1   Moon Sign Taurus

You might have to make a few sacrifices in terms of relationships, in order to keep up with a much more frenetic professional and practical pace of life. Although you may be somewhat subdued, you can still get your message across today. This is a good day, too for scoring some success in sporting activities.

21 TUESDAY
Moon Age Day 2   Moon Sign Gemini

Your main fulfilment today comes from group endeavours and happenings that throw you together with numbers of other people. Even casual acquaintances can have some interesting news to impart and there is always the possibility now that someone you haven't known well in the past could suddenly become a loyal friend.

22 WEDNESDAY
Moon Age Day 3   Moon Sign Gemini

You tend to show a very self-sacrificing face to the world today. This isn't so strange for Cancer because your consideration for others is legendary. If you have a job that involves commitment to the world at large, you ought to be able to express yourself quite fully. Isolationist tendencies need to be avoided.

23 THURSDAY
Moon Age Day 4   Moon Sign Gemini

Take advantage of planetary trends that are highlighting your chance to take a starring role. Although your practical progress could be marred in a moment-by-moment sense, you are having no difficulty whatsoever in making valuable allies. New friendships are likely to be formed at this time.

24 FRIDAY
Moon Age Day 5   Moon Sign Cancer

Almost anything you have planned for today will go well, due in no small part to the effort you are willing and able to put in. There is a strong element of luck running through most of what you do and this is definitely a time to back your hunches all the way.

25 SATURDAY

Moon Age Day 6 Moon Sign Cancer

There are now great opportunities for gain and ones that you will not want to pass by. Shopping today could lead to the discovery of genuine bargains, whilst social possibilities look particularly good. If there isn't much happening around you, chances are you are not trying hard enough.

26 SUNDAY

Moon Age Day 7 Moon Sign Leo

In terms of social encounters, the more the merrier is the rule for today. Being willing to join in with the fun should make you popular and well able to make a good impression. There is just a chance that not everyone will find you wonderful company, but nobody can have everything.

27 MONDAY

Moon Age Day 8 Moon Sign Leo

Rewarding experiences through friendship are now more likely than ever. Things may not be exactly exciting at the moment, but your imagination is working well and you can easily contribute to pepping things up in your vicinity. What you definitely have is popularity, and that isn't bad for starters.

28 TUESDAY

Moon Age Day 9 Moon Sign Leo

This is a period during which you need to let go and express yourself. Many planetary positions around you at the moment suggest that you are talking fluently and with conviction. You won't have any trouble at all getting others to listen to what you are saying, and they won't misconstrue the message.

29 WEDNESDAY

Moon Age Day 10 Moon Sign Virgo

The events of today can bring strong emotions to the surface. There is a possibility that you will react to circumstances that are more promising than might appear to be the case at first. Spreading a particular series of jobs across the day might seem sensible, but once you get started you might decide to do everything in one go.

30 THURSDAY

Moon Age Day 11 Moon Sign Virgo

A beneficial phase is present as far as career and long-term plans are concerned. Confidence isn't hard to dredge up, particularly when you are going in directions that you clearly understand. Interactions with other Water sign people, Scorpio and Pisces, as well as other Crabs, are extremely likely at this time.

May

2015

Your Month at a Glance

$+$ = Opportunities are around ● = Be on the defensive ● = Life is pretty ordinary

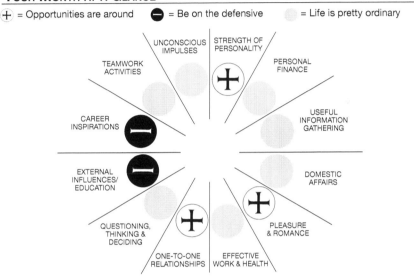

May Highs and Lows

Here I show you how the rhythms of the Moon will affect you this month. Like the tide, your energies and abilities will rise and fall with its pattern. When it is above the centre line, go for it, when it is below, you should be resting.

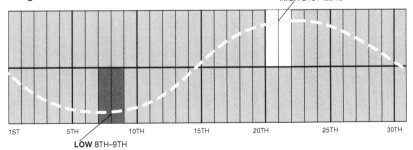

1 FRIDAY
Moon Age Day 12 Moon Sign Libra

You are now in a very good position to call the shots where future plans are concerned. What matters is that you are doing your homework, which others may not manage so well. This means your point of view is reasoned and difficult to fault. In business, you tend to be extremely shrewd at present.

2 SATURDAY
Moon Age Day 13 Moon Sign Libra

Beware that there could be disputes at home and at work. Stay away from them (though the latter will not apply if you have the weekend off). A certain wanderlust arrives at the moment, and with the better weather you may decide it is time to get out of the house. You might actively choose to spend time with friends.

3 SUNDAY
Moon Age Day 14 Moon Sign Libra

Casual contacts could be preferred today, rather than long-term ones. Your present matter-of-fact attitude does not wish to be stifled by too much depth, and practical matters are close to your heart right now. Don't be surprised if you find yourself taking a sudden and rather unexpected change in direction.

4 MONDAY
Moon Age Day 15 Moon Sign Scorpio

A good deal of what happens now depends on the say-so of others. This is slightly frustrating, because you may get a good deal of the way down a road of your own construction, only to find that you need some sort of permission to proceed. Try to remain patient and argue your case eloquently.

5 TUESDAY
Moon Age Day 16 Moon Sign Scorpio

Your ability to command attention and impress others can be put to the test today. With plenty going for you in a general sense and material situations still looking good, it's time to go for gold. Although not everyone appears to have your best interests at heart, friends come up trumps when it matters most.

6 WEDNESDAY
Moon Age Day 17 Moon Sign Sagittarius

Family matters should now be putting a smile on your face. Younger relatives especially have the ability to make you laugh, but so do many other situations and people because your sense of humour is so highly charged now. Plan for a different sort of day, with the possibility of movement and travel.

7 THURSDAY
Moon Age Day 18 Moon Sign Sagittarius

This would be an ideal time for enlisting the support of colleagues at work. If you can show them that there is a good reason for co-operation you should be able to bring them on side. Creature comforts probably mean more and the Crab now wants to bring a little luxury into life.

8 FRIDAY
Moon Age Day 19 Moon Sign Capricorn

The lunar low is almost certain to slow things down, though not disproportionately. All you really notice this month is the fact that things are not going exactly your way. If you stay away from material considerations and concentrate on having fun, the position of the Moon won't affect you at all.

9 SATURDAY
Moon Age Day 20 Moon Sign Capricorn

There are some tests of your patience to be dealt with today, but yesterday's rules still apply. Family matters are easy to deal with, but you could find a certain restless streak beginning to develop within you. Go for anything that feels different, but don't take undue risks.

10 SUNDAY
Moon Age Day 21 Moon Sign Aquarius

The more widespread and different the company you find yourself in today, the better you are likely to feel. Abandoning thoughts of security and comfort for the moment, you might be seeking to put yourself to the test in a physical sense. Communication is favoured today. Remember birthdays in the family and amongst your friends.

11 MONDAY
Moon Age Day 22 Moon Sign Aquarius

It would be best to keep your feelings out in the open today. Your zodiac sign has a tendency to bottle things up on occasion, which is very rarely the right way to proceed. You could experience some small difficulty with mechanical gadgets of one sort or another and might have to enlist some help.

12 TUESDAY
Moon Age Day 23 Moon Sign Aquarius

Today is definitely one of those times during which you get out of life almost exactly what you put into it. If you want to be lethargic, situations won't demand much of you, but you won't make the gains either. Better by far to keep moving and then to glory in the attention that comes your way.

13 WEDNESDAY
Moon Age Day 24 Moon Sign Pisces

Travel and intellectual matters of all sorts are of specific interest to you at present, at a time when you won't take at all kindly to being held in the same place. If you can't get away right now, don't despair. Your mind is working overtime and you ought to be able to work out some strategy to get a break soon.

14 THURSDAY
Moon Age Day 25 Moon Sign Pisces

You should be achieving fairly satisfactory results in practical matters. That's great, and is exactly what the Crab looks for in life at the moment. You build your world slowly but surely, and feel happy when you see the process of evolution taking place. Today, you definitely have on your thinking head.

15 FRIDAY
Moon Age Day 26 Moon Sign Aries

Better advancement is possible, probably because of all the effort you have put in recently. This doesn't necessarily refer to work. If you are a member of any organisation, you could be invited to take on a position of responsibility. One way or another, the world is looking at you with confidence.

16 SATURDAY
Moon Age Day 27 Moon Sign Aries

It feels good to be amongst groups, and maintaining a position at the centre of anything that is happening in your vicinity. Some Cancer subjects will now be thinking in terms of a new job, or consolidation with regard to present occupation. You should get a warm reception in party situations.

17 SUNDAY
Moon Age Day 28 Moon Sign Taurus

The drive to achieve is still strong, even if the planetary trends necessary to get along in an excellent manner are somewhat missing. Keep up the pressure. It isn't only your own efforts that count at present, but also those of people who care for you. By doing a job you don't care for today, you save time and trouble later.

18 MONDAY
Moon Age Day 0 Moon Sign Taurus

A boost to family matters comes along at any time now. You should begin this new week with a very positive attitude and a definite desire to succeed. If not everything goes your way at first, you can at least rely on the support of some very willing friends and, perhaps, your romantic partner.

19 TUESDAY ☿   *Moon Age Day 1 Moon Sign Gemini*

There could be intimate issues to deal with today. It's not worth letting them get you down. Maybe you ought to avoid dealing with anything too deep at the moment, opting instead for a more general view of life, in all its various hues.

20 WEDNESDAY ☿   *Moon Age Day 2 Moon Sign Gemini*

There is vital information around and you wouldn't want to miss it. For this reason alone you need to keep your ears and eyes firmly open today. It will be clear to you that not everyone you come across is telling the truth. As a result, you have to use your intuition in order to establish what is really going on.

21 THURSDAY ☿   *Moon Age Day 3 Moon Sign Cancer*

Call in a few favours today, because it looks at though almost everyone is on your side. This is a time to remember, or at least it will be if you only put in a modicum of effort. General good luck aids almost any enterprise you choose and relationships should be the cause of much happiness.

22 FRIDAY ☿   *Moon Age Day 4 Moon Sign Cancer*

This is the time to put fresh ideas to the test. You won't want to feel in any way fettered and instead show a strong determination to do what pleases you. Since you are presently so charming, it is unlikely that anyone would deliberately stand in your way. Don't be afraid of some limited and well-thought-out speculation.

23 SATURDAY ☿   *Moon Age Day 5 Moon Sign Leo*

Though your aims and objectives are generally on target today, there could be the odd frustration caused in the main by not understanding exactly what those around you are really saying. Once again, tune in that Cancer mind and listen carefully.

24 SUNDAY ☿   *Moon Age Day 6 Moon Sign Leo*

You may far better with solo endeavours today, rather than listening to what others have to say about situations. Wanting to be on your own from time to time is certainly no novelty to the Crab. Such periods merely allow you to clear your mind and to meditate about recent events.

25 MONDAY ☿ *Moon Age Day 7 Moon Sign Leo*

You are now more ready to make concessions to others, even people who have clearly messed you about in the recent past. That doesn't mean you are knuckling under in any way: something you are loath to do with the present position of Mars. What you are actually up to is establishing compromise.

26 TUESDAY ☿ *Moon Age Day 8 Moon Sign Virgo*

This is likely to be quite an upbeat phase, as your energy levels are high and your enthusiasm for life goes off the scale. Keep a sense of proportion when you are dealing with people you don't know all that well. It would be too easy to be seduced into taking financial risks that you would regret later.

27 WEDNESDAY ☿ *Moon Age Day 9 Moon Sign Virgo*

Look out for a specific financial proposition, this time one you are more than willing to look at sensibly. On a practical level, this will probably be a fairly demanding day. However, you are not short of energy or verve, so the apparent quality of your life remains high. There could be a romantic message in the evening.

28 THURSDAY ☿ *Moon Age Day 10 Moon Sign Libra*

Socially speaking, you are full of winning ways for much of today. Although you need to qualify certain matters before you push ahead, there is no reason to believe that facts and figures are being kept from you. There could be the faintest belief on your part that this is actually the case.

29 FRIDAY ☿ *Moon Age Day 11 Moon Sign Libra*

It is important to think about your next move, especially at work or with regard to major domestic changes that are in the pipeline. Casual conversations can lead to some positive realisations on your part and allow you to make minor changes now that can have positive outcomes later.

30 SATURDAY ☿ *Moon Age Day 12 Moon Sign Libra*

Any attempt to dominate relationships this weekend is likely to be met with hard stares and leading questions. Cancer doesn't usually want to prove itself to be in charge, which is why others might be puzzled and even upset. Some sacrifices may be called for, but they don't really add up to a great deal if you are realistic.

31 SUNDAY   ☿   *Moon Age Day 13 Moon Sign Scorpio*

A loved one requires some sensitive handling today and you should have sufficient natural calm to deal with almost any situation. It's time for a good old-fashioned chat, either with a family member, your partner or a friend. If you have recently decided on a new health regime, take things steadily for a while.

June

2015

Your Month at a Glance

(+) = Opportunities are around   (–) = Be on the defensive   = Life is pretty ordinary

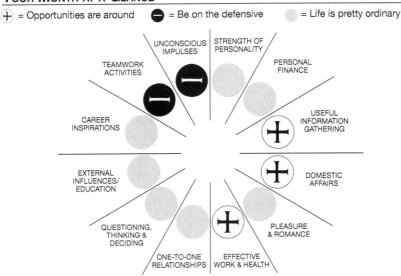

UNCONSCIOUS IMPULSES
STRENGTH OF PERSONALITY
TEAMWORK ACTIVITIES
PERSONAL FINANCE
CAREER INSPIRATIONS
USEFUL INFORMATION GATHERING
EXTERNAL INFLUENCES/ EDUCATION
DOMESTIC AFFAIRS
QUESTIONING, THINKING & DECIDING
PLEASURE & ROMANCE
ONE-TO-ONE RELATIONSHIPS
EFFECTIVE WORK & HEALTH

June Highs and Lows

Here I show you how the rhythms of the Moon will affect you this month. Like the tide, your energies and abilities will rise and fall with its pattern. When it is above the centre line, go for it, when it is below, you should be resting.

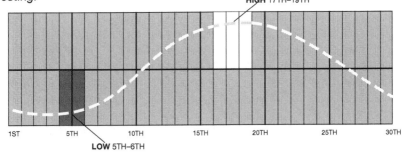

HIGH 17TH–19TH

1ST   5TH   10TH   15TH   20TH   25TH   30TH

LOW 5TH–6TH

1 MONDAY ☿ *Moon Age Day 14 Moon Sign Scorpio*

There could be a few mishaps now, especially in the workplace. You need to show some extra care and a great deal of that Cancer common sense. Don't be at all worried if you have to tell someone else to take life steadier, because whether they like it or not you are doing him or her a favour.

2 TUESDAY ☿ *Moon Age Day 15 Moon Sign Sagittarius*

Look out for a few ups and downs in finances. You need to adapt more positively to outside circumstances and also possibly recognise a few limitations that are likely to be placed upon you now. In terms of personal relationships, this week should prove to be secure and can promote greater affection generally.

3 WEDNESDAY *Moon Age Day 16 Moon Sign Sagittarius*

This is a day for enjoying the social world and for communicating ideas to others. You may need a bit more mental focus, because you are still not seeing all situations the way they really are. Confidence in your own abilities is on the increase and you might take chances today you wouldn't have considered yesterday.

4 THURSDAY ☿ *Moon Age Day 17 Moon Sign Sagittarius*

Home is most likely the place you want to be now. With the Moon in its present position, there is a great sense of nostalgia and a tendency to look back rather than forward. This is a temporary phase, in the midst of a period that carries much change, some of which can occasionally seem threatening.

5 FRIDAY ☿ *Moon Age Day 18 Moon Sign Capricorn*

The lunar low can cause you to falter regarding matters you were certain about just a short time ago. It would be sensible to remember that any negative feelings today or tomorrow are not necessarily representative of life as a whole. Take things steadily and don't try to move any mountains, not even small ones.

6 SATURDAY *Moon Age Day 19 Moon Sign Capricorn*

It could seem as though everyone else is getting ahead, leaving you at the starting post, but remember the story of the tortoise and the hare. Look around you today, do some thinking and spend time weighing up situations. When you do decide to start running, watch out world!

7 SUNDAY ☿ *Moon Age Day 20 Moon Sign Aquarius*

There is a boost to your social life today. You can make for an interesting time with other people, once the concerns of the material world have been dealt with. You could also notice an upturn in general fortune and financial strength any time now.

8 MONDAY ☿ *Moon Age Day 21 Moon Sign Aquarius*

What you tend to deal with at the start of this working week is long-term plans and the strategies necessary to get what you want from your job. Don't be too quick to jump to conclusions where the apparent actions of others are concerned. Give situations time to mature.

9 TUESDAY ☿ *Moon Age Day 22 Moon Sign Pisces*

The desire for personal freedom feels particularly strong around now, perhaps leading to you break out of some situations that no longer suit you. Not everyone is going to understand your reasoning, even though you have a particularly good ability to explain yourself at the moment.

10 WEDNESDAY ☿ *Moon Age Day 23 Moon Sign Pisces*

Midweek incentives are present and help you to latch on to any practical advantage that is around at the moment. Confidence continues to grow, though the later part of this week could bring some small reversals. In a general sense, your life is moving forwards, even though the process is steady at present.

11 THURSDAY ☿ *Moon Age Day 24 Moon Sign Aries*

Your partner could now play a more dominant role in your life, but only because that is the way you want the situation to be. In other spheres, you need to look very carefully at suggestions that are being made that somehow have a bearing on your working circumstances. Perhaps negotiation is necessary.

12 FRIDAY ☿ *Moon Age Day 25 Moon Sign Aries*

Socially speaking, this might prove to be the best time of the month. There are gains to be made by mixing with likeminded people, as well as those born of the other Water signs, which are Scorpio and Pisces. In addition, there ought to be some really inspirational types coming into your life now.

13 SATURDAY
Moon Age Day 26 Moon Sign Taurus

You want to be in charge of finances now, even though others could disagree. Don't be afraid to put forward a reasoned argument explaining your point of view. If that doesn't work, leave things alone for a day or two. You need to leave time today to talk about less serious matters and to have fun.

14 SUNDAY
Moon Age Day 27 Moon Sign Taurus

You can benefit from someone's advice, but this will not be the case unless you listen first. There is a slight tendency for you to plough your own furrow, irrespective of circumstances. Be open in your attitude and don't dismiss alternative strategies simply because they did not occur to you first.

15 MONDAY
Moon Age Day 28 Moon Sign Gemini

The start of a new working week coincides with trends that particularly favour co-operative ventures of any sort. Be willing to put yourself out for the sake of the group as a whole, whilst continuing to plough your own furrow in other ways. What you shouldn't do today is to find yourself completely out on a limb.

16 TUESDAY
Moon Age Day 29 Moon Sign Gemini

Your influence in the outside world may not appear too complete at present. As a result, you are more hesitant today and inclined to ask others what they think about situations. It isn't at all clear whether you will receive answers that please you, so it might be better to keep your own counsel in the first place.

17 WEDNESDAY
Moon Age Day 0 Moon Sign Cancer

The lunar high this month has some very practical applications, which suits you down to the ground. Your sphere of influence is strong, both at work and at home. Changes you have been wanting to implement for some time now become entirely possible, especially if you show yourself to be dynamic.

18 THURSDAY
Moon Age Day 1 Moon Sign Cancer

This is a bonus period for personal relationships and especially for love. Showing your partner or sweetheart how you feel isn't at all difficult. Since the lunar high invariably brings better-than-average luck, don't be afraid to chance your arm in some way today.

19 FRIDAY
Moon Age Day 2 Moon Sign Cancer

Make sure your desire to assert yourself more doesn't get you into hot water today. Despite the lunar high, a low-key approach to certain situations would work better than an aggressive one and would promote a more positive reaction. Your common sense will tell you what is right.

20 SATURDAY
Moon Age Day 3 Moon Sign Leo

A personal issue that seems rather up in the air could cause just a little consternation early in the day, but could be sorted out quickly. Confidence isn't lacking, even though finding something to do with it isn't at all easy right now. Friends should be especially supportive.

21 SUNDAY
Moon Age Day 4 Moon Sign Leo

A minor boost to career matters has the potential to lift your spirits no end right now. You have plenty of energy and a greater determination to push ahead, even if there are obstacles on the way. It might be necessary to resist the urge to travel today, because there are too many jobs to be done.

22 MONDAY
Moon Age Day 5 Moon Sign Virgo

A few disappointments are possible in your love life, though not if you think and look ahead. When it comes to the needs and wants of your partner you are, as always, willing to do anything you can. However, the demands that are made of you today might be excessive and could lead to some fatigue.

23 TUESDAY
Moon Age Day 6 Moon Sign Virgo

Try to avoid allowing personal matters to have a bearing on your performance in the outside world. If you are worrying about things, you won't be shining as much as you should. For this reason alone, you need to tackle any potential problem head on and defuse it before it has the chance to throw you.

24 WEDNESDAY
Moon Age Day 7 Moon Sign Virgo

You have many versatile skills just itching to be used today. With a good deal of joy coming into your life, you should be on top form. This is especially evident in personal and family attachments, where you are being sought out more and more. Someone from the past could emerge into your life again.

25 THURSDAY
Moon Age Day 8 Moon Sign Libra

With the power of the Sun now shining in your own zodiac sign, you can expect both the present and the future to look generally brighter. During this period, don't be afraid to push ahead personally to reveal some interesting situations. Your love life should be easier to predict around now.

26 FRIDAY
Moon Age Day 9 Moon Sign Libra

Work matters ought to move progressively enough, leading to some sort of minor breakthrough and a better appreciation of your place in things. Maybe you are being singled out for extra responsibility, which would at least prove to you how valuable you are when seen through the eyes of others.

27 SATURDAY
Moon Age Day 10 Moon Sign Scorpio

You will probably discover how much others can boost your ego at present, no bad thing for someone who is born under a Water sign as you are. This should be a positive sort of Saturday, filled with social and personal possibilities and replete with happenings that seem designed to cheer you.

28 SUNDAY
Moon Age Day 11 Moon Sign Scorpio

You may find yourself deliberately seeking a little romance at present and your attempts in this direction are likely to be very successful. Not only are you at your most charming right now, but you also have an armament of alluring qualities to use. General popularity is also likely.

29 MONDAY
Moon Age Day 12 Moon Sign Scorpio

This isn't the best time to stick to mundane issues. Instead, busy yourself with exciting projects and the possibilities that lie ahead personally and professionally. You should be feeling quite positive about romantic issues and probably receiving some genuine compliments.

30 TUESDAY
Moon Age Day 13 Moon Sign Sagittarius

If you insist on airing your views too much today, you might be accused of being in the wrong regarding issues that really have nothing to do with you. It's a fine line to walk between having your say and overdoing things. When a little timely advice arrives, it might be sensible to listen.

July

2015

YOUR MONTH AT A GLANCE

$(+)$ = Opportunities are around   ● = Be on the defensive   ● = Life is pretty ordinary

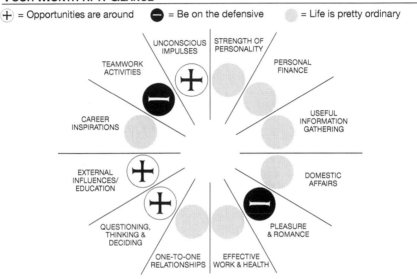

UNCONSCIOUS IMPULSES — STRENGTH OF PERSONALITY — TEAMWORK ACTIVITIES — PERSONAL FINANCE — CAREER INSPIRATIONS — USEFUL INFORMATION GATHERING — EXTERNAL INFLUENCES/ EDUCATION — DOMESTIC AFFAIRS — QUESTIONING, THINKING & DECIDING — PLEASURE & ROMANCE — ONE-TO-ONE RELATIONSHIPS — EFFECTIVE WORK & HEALTH

JULY HIGHS AND LOWS

Here I show you how the rhythms of the Moon will affect you this month. Like the tide, your energies and abilities will rise and fall with its pattern. When it is above the centre line, go for it, when it is below, you should be resting.

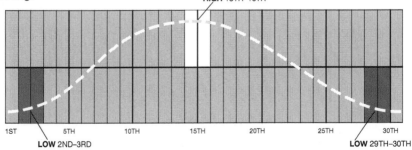

HIGH 15TH–16TH

1ST   5TH   10TH   15TH   20TH   25TH   30TH

LOW 2ND–3RD   **LOW** 29TH–30TH

1 WEDNESDAY
Moon Age Day 14 Moon Sign Sagittarius

You can bend career situations your own way and stand a chance of making a good impression on others at the moment. Confidence is certainly not lacking, though you could also discover that someone you counted as a friend is not doing you any favours. All the same, don't react.

2 THURSDAY
Moon Age Day 15 Moon Sign Capricorn

Whilst the lunar low is around it might be sensible to allow your partner or another family member to deal with some of the major issues on the home front. Although you can hold your own at work, there might not be the same feeling of progress that has been around for quite a few days now.

3 FRIDAY
Moon Age Day 16 Moon Sign Capricorn

Since you are not in the mood for practical matters, the lunar low doesn't really restrict you very much. This is an ideal time to plan a journey, or to decide that the time is right for alterations and changes on the domestic scene. Treat a friend today and expect some sort of gift yourself.

4 SATURDAY
Moon Age Day 17 Moon Sign Aquarius

This could be a good day for family get-togethers or reunions of some sort, as a slightly nostalgic streak takes over. There is perhaps nothing wrong with looking on the internet to see if you can locate some of those buddies you haven't seen for years. If you find them, be prepared for one or two surprises.

5 SUNDAY
Moon Age Day 18 Moon Sign Aquarius

This is another of those periods during which you are happy to be in the social spotlight. Right now, the Crab is more gregarious than usual. Don't panic though, because you still maintain that slight inner reserve that marks you out as being different from more showy zodiac signs.

6 MONDAY
Moon Age Day 19 Moon Sign Pisces

Emotional tensions could be present, maybe caused by the way colleagues are behaving. Although you demonstrate great loyalty this month, it won't always be coming back to you in the way you would wish or expect. Some situations need a definite dose of intuition.

7 TUESDAY
Moon Age Day 20 Moon Sign Pisces

The more ambitious you are today, the better you are likely to get on. Keep your ears open, because even the most casual of conversations could be carrying some surprising but useful news. In any situation, it can be quite crucial to strike whilst the iron is hot. At work, you can be a force to be reckoned with.

8 WEDNESDAY
Moon Age Day 21 Moon Sign Aries

There is quite a lot of progress to be made today, particularly at work. At the same time, you should be champing at the bit with regard to home-based alterations. With the best of the summer weather still to come, it could be that you are altering the shape or composition of your garden. You are very creative at present.

9 THURSDAY
Moon Age Day 22 Moon Sign Aries

Any opportunity to broaden your horizons in a general sense should be grabbed with both hands today, yet another indication that Cancer subjects are in a holiday frame of mind. If everyday responsibilities make this impossible, do at least try to get some change and diversity into your life during social hours.

10 FRIDAY
Moon Age Day 23 Moon Sign Taurus

You now find yourself at the start of a go-ahead period and a time during which your progress depends almost entirely on the amount of effort you are willing to put in. You can contribute to little family triumphs across the coming weekend and you do need to ensure there are moments during which you can simply think.

11 SATURDAY
Moon Age Day 24 Moon Sign Taurus

The weekend ought to find you in a generally good frame of mind, mainly because circumstances now favour your efforts. You are not the least bit frightened of hard work, even if the weekend means a possible break for you. This would be a good time to tackle some sort of job in or around your home.

12 SUNDAY
Moon Age Day 25 Moon Sign Taurus

You are in a very good position to influence others, particularly at work. Even if a degree of coercion is necessary, as long as you know the end genuinely does justify the means, you should go ahead. Once any work is out of the way, you might be especially pleased to be out of doors.

13 MONDAY
Moon Age Day 26   Moon Sign Gemini

The most casual of meetings could turn into something much more interesting. Although there are one or two people around now who are not all that trustworthy, you can see through such individuals. The most appealing thing about today is the sheer volume of work you can get through.

14 TUESDAY
Moon Age Day 27   Moon Sign Gemini

You have a strong thirst for fresh experiences now. Seeking out change and variety in your life is likely to be extremely important and there are very few difficult trends to deal with right now. Although you are good at problem solving, you might have to seek out an expert during today or tomorrow.

15 WEDNESDAY
Moon Age Day 28   Moon Sign Cancer

It's time to push ahead with your dreams and schemes, because if you are going to make anything of them this is the most likely period. Cancer is especially unsettled today, though not in a negative sense. Travel has been a distinct possibility so far this month and is even more likely now.

16 THURSDAY
Moon Age Day 0   Moon Sign Cancer

Most everyday issues go according to plan and progress should be generally smooth. You can negotiate potential difficulties without really recognising they are present and should also enjoy a high degree of popularity in a general sense. Best of all, Lady Luck could pay you a visit.

17 FRIDAY
Moon Age Day 1   Moon Sign Leo

Right now you feel like doing something to please yourself, rather than running around assisting others all the time. You are perfectly entitled to be selfish once in a while and you ought to be able to expect just a little support. If it isn't forthcoming, have a word in the right ear.

18 SATURDAY
Moon Age Day 2   Moon Sign Leo

Though your sympathies are easily stirred today, you won't be able to help everyone out. Just bear in mind that you usually tend to do a good deed each day. Friends will be seeking your special support, in particular, but it may be necessary to tell some of them there is nothing you can do.

19 SUNDAY
Moon Age Day 3 Moon Sign Leo

This is a time when you can get the best from others, and a period during which you are quite willing to allow others to put themselves out on your behalf. Rules and regulations could so easily get on your nerves today and it might be all you can manage not to give someone in authority a piece of your mind.

20 MONDAY
Moon Age Day 4 Moon Sign Virgo

Minor challenges and even confrontations can be expected at work, which means you have to put on a good show in order to hold your own. Every good Crab knows that there is more than one way to skin a cat, however, so turn the intuition up full, stay cool and wait for the appropriate moment.

21 TUESDAY
Moon Age Day 5 Moon Sign Virgo

Though you are clearly ready to work like the dickens for what you want at present, it will appear today that at least some other people are not prepared to put in the same amount of effort. Don't get hung up on details this week. What really matters is the broad overview of life.

22 WEDNESDAY
Moon Age Day 6 Moon Sign Libra

In the financial world, you need to be very aware of whom you trust today. Stay away from deals that look somewhat bent, because they probably are. You wouldn't want to have anything to do with situations that mean you getting on the wrong side of the law, no matter how trivial they might be. Stick with friends.

23 THURSDAY
Moon Age Day 7 Moon Sign Libra

Think about spending an evening at home today, after what is likely to be a fairly demanding sort of day. The support of your loved ones is always important to you and you do need a certain amount of rest if you are to work to the best of your abilities. You may even decide to spend a few hours alone now.

24 FRIDAY
Moon Age Day 8 Moon Sign Libra

It may surprise others that you appear to give in to specific demands that are made today. Those who want to protect you the most will be the ones who make a fuss, but they don't really understand the situation. For your part, staying calm is not a problem and you have life fully under control.

25 SATURDAY
Moon Age Day 9   Moon Sign Scorpio

You almost certainly need more excitement than your homestead can offer this weekend. Although you are a home bird for much of the year, it is around now that you feel a definite desire to get out into the country, or even more beneficially, to the coast. All you have to do is persuade someone to go with you.

26 SUNDAY
Moon Age Day 10   Moon Sign Scorpio

Personal relationships might not be doing you quite as many favours as you could have wished today. It is possible that things are a little strained, and a slightly odd attitude on your part probably will not be helping things too much. There ought to be plenty of confidence to do the right thing socially.

27 MONDAY
Moon Age Day 11   Moon Sign Sagittarius

The pace of life now speeds up noticeably and you enter a working week that carries a good deal of excitement at first. Make the most of it though, because later on things become much quieter. Routines could very easily get on your nerves today and you need to ring the changes as much as possible.

28 TUESDAY
Moon Age Day 12   Moon Sign Sagittarius

There is a positive focus on getting things done, even if some people don't seem to be helping out as much as they might. Instinctively, you are pushing on ahead of the lunar low, due tomorrow. As a homemaker, you reign supreme right now and have a desire to make everyone comfortable.

29 WEDNESDAY
Moon Age Day 13   Moon Sign Capricorn

It could easily feel as if others are getting ahead a good deal faster than you are, and this is actually the case, but only for the moment. Look ahead, plan and make the most of social prospects, which remain good. By the evening, you may be feeling like seeking out company.

30 THURSDAY
Moon Age Day 14   Moon Sign Capricorn

Although life is quieter now that the Moon is in your opposite zodiac sign, it could also feel a good deal more comfortable, at least in some ways. You won't have to think too hard at the moment and are willing to put some concerns to one side. By the time you go back to them, they might have disappeared.

31 FRIDAY
Moon Age Day 15   Moon Sign Aquarius

You ought to represent a lively presence on the social scene this Friday, and will certainly be enjoying the warm days and friendly, outdoor evenings. Avoid confrontations with your partner or someone else who is special to you. It won't do any good at all to lose your temper.

August

2015

Your Month at a Glance

$\oplus$ = Opportunities are around   ⊖ = Be on the defensive   ⬤ = Life is pretty ordinary

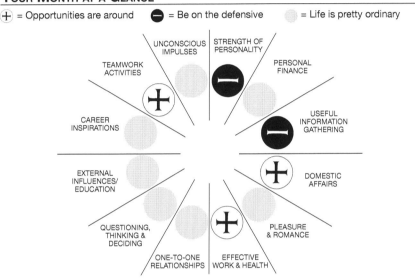

UNCONSCIOUS IMPULSES

STRENGTH OF PERSONALITY

TEAMWORK ACTIVITIES

PERSONAL FINANCE

CAREER INSPIRATIONS

USEFUL INFORMATION GATHERING

EXTERNAL INFLUENCES/ EDUCATION

DOMESTIC AFFAIRS

QUESTIONING, THINKING & DECIDING

PLEASURE & ROMANCE

ONE-TO-ONE RELATIONSHIPS

EFFECTIVE WORK & HEALTH

August Highs and Lows

Here I show you how the rhythms of the Moon will affect you this month. Like the tide, your energies and abilities will rise and fall with its pattern. When it is above the centre line, go for it, when it is below, you should be resting.

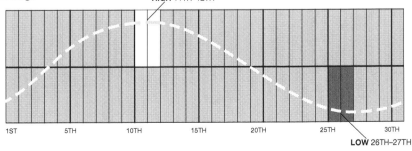

HIGH 11TH–12TH

1ST   5TH   10TH   15TH   20TH   25TH   30TH

LOW 26TH–27TH

1 SATURDAY
Moon Age Day 16   Moon Sign Aquarius

There is a strong emphasis now on broadening your horizons and on making sure you are in the right place at the best time to get ahead. Not everyone proves to be equally helpful today, but if you turn in the right direction you can be sure of the sort of support you are looking for.

2 SUNDAY
Moon Age Day 17   Moon Sign Pisces

Domestic responsibilities could so easily get in the way of things you would rather be doing. It pays dividends to think in advance and to make sure all those chores are out of the way so that you can concentrate on having fun. Compliments could be coming your way from unlikely directions.

3 MONDAY
Moon Age Day 18   Moon Sign Pisces

Conversations of all kinds should be appealing today. When they are applied to your present business acumen, you should be able to get ahead in a very positive manner. There is quite a restless streak about you and there is no doubt that there are times you would rather be travelling than staying around to attend to responsibilities.

4 TUESDAY
Moon Age Day 19   Moon Sign Aries

Your powers of attraction should be stronger than ever today. Compliments come from a host of different directions, but nothing being said is likely to turn your steady Cancer head. Intuition is strong, so you definitely know when someone is stringing you along, which could happen at this time.

5 WEDNESDAY
Moon Age Day 20   Moon Sign Aries

There are many changes around just now and your greatest desire is to keep life on an even keel. Actually, it could be the case that you are trying too hard. Allow things to happen in their own good time. If you are constantly reacting, it is possible that you are not using either your intuition or your common sense enough.

6 THURSDAY
Moon Age Day 21   Moon Sign Aries

Keep on looking for those wide, open spaces. This is a holiday time generally, but turns out to be an especially good time for you to take a break. If you can't get away from the rat race, at least leave some time free at some stage during the day. Even a walk in the park would be better than nothing.

7 FRIDAY
Moon Age Day 22 Moon Sign Taurus

Your assertive nature now starts to show. This will come as a genuine surprise to some people and might be just what you need to wrong-foot the opposition. You won't take kindly to being told what to do, particularly in situations where you know you should be in the driving seat.

8 SATURDAY
Moon Age Day 23 Moon Sign Taurus

This could be the high point of the month where travel is concerned, and will see many Crabs packing their bags and jetting off. It doesn't really matter how near or far you go; the important thing is that you have worked hard of late and could do with a genuine change of pace.

9 SUNDAY
Moon Age Day 24 Moon Sign Gemini

A long-standing commitment could need urgent attention today. There is plenty on your agenda now, but if you spread your commitments a little, or even offload one or two of them on to willing volunteers, you will find the going easier. There are positive financial influences around that can be exploited.

10 MONDAY
Moon Age Day 25 Moon Sign Gemini

Life could take on a rather so-so quality today, unless you put in that extra bit of effort that can make all the difference. Don't be willing to accept second-best, either from yourself or others. The urge to see new places is still around you and you might decide to make use of this period for travelling around.

11 TUESDAY
Moon Age Day 26 Moon Sign Cancer

The lunar high brings one of the high points of August. In today's bigger undertakings, you should discover that good luck is on your side and things just seem to fall into place. Getting your own way in group situations should be especially easy and remains so for a few days.

12 WEDNESDAY
Moon Age Day 27 Moon Sign Cancer

Press on with whatever activities you have planned and assume that things are going to work out the way you would wish. In the main, this is likely to be the case. This could be the best day of all for financial ventures and is also a notable period in terms of your overall popularity.

13 THURSDAY
Moon Age Day 28 Moon Sign Leo

Don't let relationships at work become strained. There's only so much you can do, and if others prove to be awkward against all the odds you cannot change the situation. However, if you are open in your attitude and remain willing to discuss situations, you should bring people round easily.

14 FRIDAY
Moon Age Day 29 Moon Sign Leo

The world outside your door continues to be busy and it looks as though you are doing all you can to be involved. This might not be easy. The demands that are being made of you today come from family members and possibly friends. Business and pleasure can mix well for the Crab, but not today.

15 SATURDAY
Moon Age Day 0 Moon Sign Leo

Your sense of adventure grows and grows. Since it is likely you are not at work today, do something really different and make sure you have allies who can make the whole situation that much more enjoyable. Your general level of confidence isn't as high as it might appear, but you won't give any indication to others.

16 SUNDAY
Moon Age Day 1 Moon Sign Virgo

The focus is on leisure, though possibly of a more robust sort today. The fun side of your nature is definitely on display, which is why you are less inclined to want to be alone at the moment. It is the lighter aspects of life that bring the greatest rewards at present and which seem so supportive.

17 MONDAY
Moon Age Day 2 Moon Sign Virgo

Take advantage of planetary trends and you could turn into something of a whiz kid today. That's fine, but beware that not all your suppositions turn out to be correct. It would be more than sensible to check and recheck details, especially where any work-related matter is concerned.

18 TUESDAY
Moon Age Day 3 Moon Sign Libra

The best thing you can be today is busy. Financial potential is good and you might find yourself more willing to take chances than would sometimes be the case. Pace yourself and do things in your usual methodical way. The time is right for romantic overtures at some stage during the day.

19 WEDNESDAY · *Moon Age Day 4 Moon Sign Libra*

Don't be surprised if you are a little uncertain of what people are saying today. It isn't that they are being deliberately obtuse, more that you are not quite as sharp as would usually be the case. In some respects, it will be necessary to rely on the strength of your intuition, which is heightened again now.

20 THURSDAY · *Moon Age Day 5 Moon Sign Libra*

There are signs that there is more than a small element of luck behind proceedings today. A combination of wit, instinct and understanding is in evidence, giving you the edge in almost any situation. Routines are not for you at present, at a time when you would be more willing than ever to seek excitement.

21 FRIDAY · *Moon Age Day 6 Moon Sign Scorpio*

This might prove to be another generally beneficial day. Money matters should be easy to deal with and the present position of the Sun might indicate some cash coming your way that you didn't expect. In public situations, you are tending to speak out with confidence, offering a sound counsel to almost anyone.

22 SATURDAY · *Moon Age Day 7 Moon Sign Scorpio*

You will be able to get the best from relatives and friends, though it is possible that associates could cause problems if you are a weekend worker. This is a time for travel or thoughts of travel. Chances are that you are already making the very best of all opportunities to be out of doors.

23 SUNDAY · *Moon Age Day 8 Moon Sign Sagittarius*

The typical Cancer traits that are so much a part of your nature are emphasised today. This means you are happy at home, always willing to listen to what other people have to say and interested in some of the deeper aspects of life. Cancer is a thinker at present, and probably not too loud or even over sociable.

24 MONDAY · *Moon Age Day 9 Moon Sign Sagittarius*

Keep your options open, especially at work. There could be a chance of advancement, which you would see as being entirely beneficial. The only thing that could hinder you is a lack of flexibility. Although you still want to do things your own way, a touch of compromise marks the difference between moderate gains and significant ones.

25 TUESDAY
Moon Age Day 10 Moon Sign Sagittarius

Your desire for excitement and romance can so easily be fulfilled today. A strong highlight seems to be your love life, which proves to be especially so in the case of Cancer subjects who are looking for a new relationship. It might be correct to say that a holiday romance is on the cards.

26 WEDNESDAY
Moon Age Day 11 Moon Sign Capricorn

The pace of life for the Crab is now slower than you would wish. This is the legacy of the lunar low. There are good aspects to this period though. Your ability to view situations dispassionately is very good and you would be unlikely to make any unforced errors.

27 THURSDAY
Moon Age Day 12 Moon Sign Capricorn

Things are still not moving quite as fast as you would wish, a fact that could lead to some small frustrations as the day wears on. Keep your eye on the ball, particularly when at work and don't allow others to steal a march on you. Your generally steady approach to life is an advantage.

28 FRIDAY
Moon Age Day 13 Moon Sign Aquarius

Although you have some good ideas right now, you could have more than a little difficulty explaining them to other people. The path ahead looks somewhat uncertain and you would not wish to commit yourself to any course of action that looks filled with potential problems. Some reserve is in evidence.

29 SATURDAY
Moon Age Day 14 Moon Sign Aquarius

Some helpful news is likely to arrive regarding at least one of your major ambitions. You relish challenges and will be much more competitive than was the case last week. Because you glide effortlessly between states of being, you won't upset anyone on the way. To find support today is as easy as blinking.

30 SUNDAY
Moon Age Day 15 Moon Sign Pisces

Though your thought processes are quick and you don't lack sound judgement, you can be thrown by the slightly quirky behaviour of someone you know well. Allow a degree of latitude, because he or she might be going through a hard time you don't altogether understand. Maybe you should ask a leading question.

31 MONDAY

Meetings with others should represent pleasurable events and bring you closer to an understanding of what makes them tick. Any opportunity to get beneath the surface of a situation is likely to be grasped firmly by you at present. There are some small surprises in store, which should prove favourable.

September

2015

YOUR MONTH AT A GLANCE

⊕ = Opportunities are around   ⊖ = Be on the defensive   ⚬ = Life is pretty ordinary

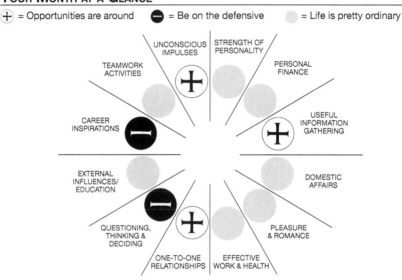

SEPTEMBER HIGHS AND LOWS

Here I show you how the rhythms of the Moon will affect you this month. Like the tide, your energies and abilities will rise and fall with its pattern. When it is above the centre line, go for it, when it is below, you should be resting.

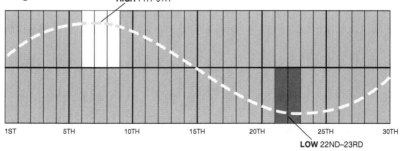

HIGH 7TH–9TH

1ST   5TH   10TH   15TH   20TH   25TH   30TH

LOW 22ND–23RD

1 TUESDAY
Moon Age Day 17   Moon Sign Aries

You certainly intend to be heard today and you won't be backward when it comes to letting people know. There is a chance you could unintentionally cause offence, so do your best not to. The present position of Mars can take just a little of the recent charm out of your nature.

2 WEDNESDAY
Moon Age Day 18   Moon Sign Aries

Things are looking up. Although there are still some problems around, you tend to deal with them quickly and efficiently. This will probably be the most successful day of the working week and offers you the chance to take on new responsibilities. Don't fight shy of showing what you can do.

3 THURSDAY
Moon Age Day 19   Moon Sign Taurus

Your sense of adventure remains strong and you have the ability to lead others into something particularly spectacular around now. People are quite naturally turning to you for advice on how to live their own lives. You should also be doing very well now in the romantic stakes.

4 FRIDAY
Moon Age Day 20   Moon Sign Taurus

This would be as good a time as any to take an idea you have had recently and to run with it. With some fairly influential people around, you could ask for endorsements and can also make headway against the odds. The Crab is irrepressible at present, maybe more so than at any time this year.

5 SATURDAY
Moon Age Day 21   Moon Sign Gemini

You can't please all of the people all of the time, a saying that is likely to make real sense to you today. There are times when it is pointless trying and in the end all you can do is to be certain you are doing your best. Some people won't even believe that you're doing that, but that's the way life is.

6 SUNDAY
Moon Age Day 22   Moon Sign Gemini

You are probably making a greater impression on some people than you think. This is especially likely to be the case with those who are your intended romantic targets. The Crab is not showy or particularly noisy, but you can still let people know you are around. Your confidence is almost palpable today.

7 MONDAY
Moon Age Day 23   Moon Sign Cancer

Today the lunar high really comes into full force, supercharging your nature and making it easy for you to see the way ahead. If you are single and have been wanting to ask someone out, this is the time to do it. Those in longer term relationships should be getting special support from their partners.

8 TUESDAY
Moon Age Day 24   Moon Sign Cancer

You need to be in the right place at the right time if you really want situations to pay off now. This isn't at all difficult, because your intuition is sparkling, telling you where to go and what to do when you get there. It might be suggested that you are virtually flying on automatic pilot today.

9 WEDNESDAY
Moon Age Day 25   Moon Sign Cancer

If you refuse to listen to others today, it's possible that you are doing both them and you a definite disfavour. Even people you haven't thought of as being the types to offer advice have some interesting things to say now. On a different tack, it's not an auspicious time for communication, so make sure that letters are posted and emails sent.

10 THURSDAY
Moon Age Day 26   Moon Sign Leo

Extreme restlessness is possible today. This is because you have been firing on all cylinders for a few days and might now find yourself with time on your hands. That's great, because it means you can find some way to unwind. Grab a friend and do something that isn't important, but is enjoyable all the same.

11 FRIDAY
Moon Age Day 27   Moon Sign Leo

Where communication is concerned, you have it within you to get the best from others today. You have a natural tendency at present to fight for the underdog, but first make certain your support is justified in each case. Finances are favoured today.

12 SATURDAY
Moon Age Day 28   Moon Sign Virgo

You have plenty of opportunity at the moment simply to be yourself. You might think that the real you is not interesting or inspiring, but it's what others think that counts. Show some caution in business dealings. Don't be taken for a fool or you could lose money.

13 SUNDAY
Moon Age Day 0 Moon Sign Virgo

You have certain duties to fulfil and not all of them are equally enjoyable. However, these should not take the edge off your ability to enjoy this Sunday. Although the inclination to travel has been strong within you for some weeks now, today's inclination is more a stay-at-home one.

14 MONDAY
Moon Age Day 1 Moon Sign Virgo

Work and practical matters could provide a few frustrations today. Be prepared for not everything to go your way, which won't please you at all. Your best area of focus today would be towards your social life, which offers far more in the way of enjoyment than employment presently can.

15 TUESDAY
Moon Age Day 2 Moon Sign Libra

Though you might feel slightly less in command today, the fact is that you can still turn situations around and won't have any trouble predicting the way others are likely to react. With plenty to play for in the financial stakes, you won't be taking undue risks, but might be considering calculated ones.

16 WEDNESDAY
Moon Age Day 3 Moon Sign Libra

There are some good ideas coming along today, and these in turn might lead to a slightly stronger financial situation in the not-too-distant future. Your mind is ingenious and capable of dealing with several different matters at the same time. Don't allow yourself to be restricted.

17 THURSDAY
Moon Age Day 4 Moon Sign Scorpio

Mentally speaking, you are ready for any challenge. Your wit is razor sharp and you represent especially good company. If you are planning a late holiday this year, now is as good a time as any to get started. Don't worry too much about frequent interruptions to your plans today. These are grist to the mill.

18 FRIDAY
Moon Age Day 5 Moon Sign Scorpio

There is no real sign of your life slowing down today, which means carefully pacing yourself and being selective about what you choose to take on. You can benefit socially and even personally from being on the move, even if the movement is only in your mind for the moment.

19 SATURDAY   ☿   *Moon Age Day 6   Moon Sign Scorpio*

Now finances are likely to be looking stronger, making it more or less inevitable that this is one area of life that grabs your attention. Don't try to get everything done all at once, but be willing to spread jobs out during the day. Some exciting invitations are on the cards, but you might have to put yourself out to accept them.

20 SUNDAY   ☿   *Moon Age Day 7   Moon Sign Sagittarius*

The good things in life are easier to acquire, though when you have them, the appeal could soon disappear. In essence, you are opting for simplicity this Sunday and can gain the most from the least complicated possibilities. Money is not your main motive for the moment.

21 MONDAY   ☿   *Moon Age Day 8   Moon Sign Sagittarius*

Be prepared to encounter some resistance to your ideas and plans. If this turns out to be the case, maybe you should look not at what you are saying, but the way you are expressing yourself. Simply rein back the enthusiasm a little and you can get almost anyone to agree with you.

22 TUESDAY   ☿   *Moon Age Day 9   Moon Sign Capricorn*

There are signs that it might be best to suspend major activities wherever you can, at least until Thursday. That means giving yourself more spare time, some of which you can spend building broken bridges, particularly in the family. The fact that not everyone is seeing eye to eye at present isn't your fault, but you might feel some responsibility for it.

23 WEDNESDAY ☿   *Moon Age Day 10   Moon Sign Capricorn*

Today could be another slightly quieter day and definitely not one during which you should take any financial risks. Keep it light and steady, no matter what you decide to do. If there are parties going on somewhere near you, you will want to join in, despite the fact that your social skills seem somewhat diminished at present.

24 THURSDAY   ☿   *Moon Age Day 11   Moon Sign Aquarius*

A powerful desire to get things done is highlighted today. Avoid getting on the wrong side of people who definitely have influence upon your life. Today offers social highlights, even if you have to create some of them yourself. Leave some time for romance and let someone know how special he or she is.

25 FRIDAY ☿ *Moon Age Day 12 Moon Sign Aquarius*

This could prove to be a time of luck as far as money is concerned. This doesn't mean you should go out and put your money on the next horse running, but if you keep your eyes open you could be in for a small windfall of some sort. Getting your own way in discussions should be easy enough under present trends.

26 SATURDAY ☿ *Moon Age Day 13 Moon Sign Pisces*

You are likely to be extremely busy today and so finding the time necessary to spend with loved ones won't be at all easy. Conforming to expectations at work isn't hard, but not everyone will appear to have your best interests at heart. By the evening you may decide that some sort of treat to yourself is in order.

27 SUNDAY ☿ *Moon Age Day 14 Moon Sign Pisces*

Group and co-operative matters could go slightly less smoothly than you anticipate, so it is necessary to keep your wits about you today. You can certainly stand out in a crowd, but possibly for all the wrong reasons. It is likely that if you feel threatened in any way, you will seek a degree of solitude.

28 MONDAY ☿ *Moon Age Day 15 Moon Sign Aries*

Much of your life is tailored towards practical matters this Monday, perhaps leaving less time for personal enjoyment than you might have wished. Avoid confusion by saying what you feel up front. Once you have made up your mind to any course of action, it would be best to stick to it.

29 TUESDAY ☿ *Moon Age Day 16 Moon Sign Aries*

Despite mostly passive social trends, you can still be very engaging and fun to have around. Spending time with your partner could seem appealing, though if you are mixing freely with others, they are likely to be people you already know. Actually getting your own way with this regard might not be too easy.

30 WEDNESDAY ☿ *Moon Age Day 17 Moon Sign Taurus*

There are all manner of new opportunities presenting themselves at the moment and you won't want to miss out on any of them. Confidence is present in great measure, plus an ability to hear comments that make all the difference to your own ideas. Some would call you nosy now, but who cares?

October

2015

YOUR MONTH AT A GLANCE

(+) = Opportunities are around   ⊖ = Be on the defensive   ○ = Life is pretty ordinary

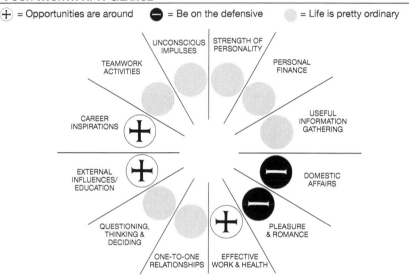

- UNCONSCIOUS IMPULSES
- STRENGTH OF PERSONALITY
- TEAMWORK ACTIVITIES
- PERSONAL FINANCE
- CAREER INSPIRATIONS
- USEFUL INFORMATION GATHERING
- EXTERNAL INFLUENCES/ EDUCATION
- DOMESTIC AFFAIRS
- QUESTIONING, THINKING & DECIDING
- PLEASURE & ROMANCE
- ONE-TO-ONE RELATIONSHIPS
- EFFECTIVE WORK & HEALTH

OCTOBER HIGHS AND LOWS

Here I show you how the rhythms of the Moon will affect you this month. Like the tide, your energies and abilities will rise and fall with its pattern. When it is above the centre line, go for it, when it is below, you should be resting.

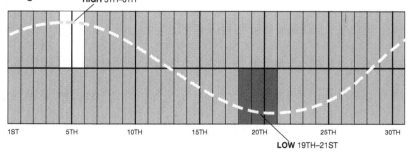

HIGH 5TH–6TH

1ST   5TH   10TH   15TH   20TH   25TH   30TH

LOW 19TH–21ST

1 THURSDAY   *Moon Age Day 18 Moon Sign Taurus*

There are good reasons for getting annoyed if you are restricted in any way today. The truth is that the Crab knows where it wants to go and won't take kindly to being prevented from doing so. All the same, you retain the essential popularity that is your usual lot.

2 FRIDAY   *Moon Age Day 19 Moon Sign Gemini*

Your general capabilities are not up to scratch, or at least that's the way it seems from your perspective. Actually, you are probably doing a great deal better than you realise. Towards the end of the day, you should discover that things are brightening up generally, but all the same don't take any undue risks.

3 SATURDAY   *Moon Age Day 20 Moon Sign Gemini*

This is the time to ditch whatever has been holding you back. If this is going to prove awkward or embarrassing, you might have to think things through first. What you can't do is carry on down a road that definitely isn't the right one for you. Comfort and security mean a great deal by the evening.

4 SUNDAY   *Moon Age Day 21 Moon Sign Gemini*

Your sense of adventure is strong this Sunday. You almost certainly will not want to stay at home and put your feet up. This is the sort of period during which you set yourself a challenge and then go out and win. Advice from others is well intentioned, but you probably don't want it at all.

5 MONDAY   *Moon Age Day 22 Moon Sign Cancer*

Once the green light comes on there is little that can hold you back now. Not only creative, you are also tinged with a sort of genius right now, which ought to allow you to think up some amazing ways of getting ahead. Popularity in social situations ought to be going off the scale.

6 TUESDAY   *Moon Age Day 23 Moon Sign Cancer*

It's time to get busy. With energy levels particularly high and a genuine desire to get things done, you can probably start very early in the day. Once the practical necessities of the day are sorted, it's time to go out and have fun. You probably won't stop moving from the time you wake up until the moment you go to bed again.

7 WEDNESDAY ☿ *Moon Age Day 24 Moon Sign Leo*

Relationships of almost any sort can be emotionally uplifting, but where love and romance are concerned, the world should be your oyster right now. Confidence is not lacking, though it is represented better in personal rather than professional situations. You could be on the receiving end of a very special favour.

8 THURSDAY ☿ *Moon Age Day 25 Moon Sign Leo*

Only you can decide whether to believe everything you hear today. A good dose of scepticism proves to be necessary, because there are tall tales around. Just when you think everyone is talking nonsense, the silliest story of all might just turn out to be true.

9 FRIDAY ☿ *Moon Age Day 26 Moon Sign Virgo*

Finances are well starred today, and gaining more resources could be your main priority. Although it might seem at first that there is nowhere you can get more cash, your present logical and methodical approach should win out in the end. In social encounters, you tend to shine now.

10 SATURDAY ☿ *Moon Age Day 27 Moon Sign Virgo*

Important discussions or negotiations can turn up trumps for you today and could lead you to find a way forward professionally that hasn't been an option before. Talk, talk and more talk is what matters for the Crab today, because that's the only way you are going to alter anything.

11 SUNDAY ☿ *Moon Age Day 28 Moon Sign Virgo*

Because there is much to get done today, specific issues may have to be rerouted or even changed altogether. There can be a feeling of dislocation and a tendency to fight shy of things you don't want to face. Talk to someone in the know, if you think it might be helpful.

12 MONDAY *Moon Age Day 29 Moon Sign Libra*

Happy encounters with people from the past are quite likely to take place at any time now. There is a sense of nostalgia that is difficult to define, yet which can even be of use if you view it positively. One thing is certain: you should not dwell on the past, because that could lead to unfair comparisons in your mind.

13 TUESDAY
Moon Age Day 0 Moon Sign Libra

Getting what you want, either in a professional or a personal sense, should not prove to be at all difficult now. You have strong willpower and a determination that cannot be bettered by anyone. Decide what you want from life and find unique ways to achieve your objectives.

14 WEDNESDAY
Moon Age Day 1 Moon Sign Scorpio

You show great efficiency today and can be sure that whatever you tackle gets done well and quickly. Don't be at all surprised if your popularity is going off the scale and make the most of improving social trends. There are some very talkative people around at the moment and you are not the least of them.

15 THURSDAY
Moon Age Day 2 Moon Sign Scorpio

The desire you are presently feeling to broaden your horizons can prove to be a very good incentive at this time. Few situations should be holding you back, though you are likely to find some difficulty with younger family members, wayward friends and possibly a person who constantly embarrasses you.

16 FRIDAY
Moon Age Day 3 Moon Sign Scorpio

What marks today apart is that you are so efficient in almost everything you do. This means that most jobs are easy to address and the sheer number of successes that you score is legion. Avoid rows with people, particularly individuals you have always found to be basically unreasonable in their attitude.

17 SATURDAY
Moon Age Day 4 Moon Sign Sagittarius

Don't take on too many commitments in a short space of time today. The fact is that you may become overwhelmed, which won't help at all in the longer term. Someone you know well is behaving in a less than typical manner and you may need to use one or two sharp words in order to get them to listen.

18 SUNDAY
Moon Age Day 5 Moon Sign Sagittarius

Everyday communications now provide you with the ammunition that becomes incentive in the days and weeks ahead. Many Crabs will be coming up with ingenious ideas right now. These need to be analysed and sorted, before you push on towards significant new objectives.

19 MONDAY
Moon Age Day 6 Moon Sign Capricorn

With the lunar low around, it feels as if the brakes have suddenly been applied. You cannot expect to make the same sort of progress that has been possible recently and will be forced into a much more contemplative frame of mind. Confrontation should be absolutely avoided, especially at work.

20 TUESDAY
Moon Age Day 7 Moon Sign Capricorn

There are obligations about, some of which you feel strongly. Where work is concerned, do a reasonable amount at any one time and then ring the changes. Having to come back to things later merely allows you to start fresh again and to utilise new ideas and incentives that come along.

21 WEDNESDAY
Moon Age Day 8 Moon Sign Capricorn

What matters at the moment is getting your own way, and this shows from the very start of the day. This trend alone could lead to some confrontation, if others decide that their point of view is more valid than yours. There is much to be said for staying determined to get new ideas out into the open.

22 THURSDAY
Moon Age Day 9 Moon Sign Aquarius

The challenge today is keeping up with rivals, though you will relish the chance to lock antlers with at least one person. As long as you remain convinced of your own abilities, you are likely to come out on top. In the social sphere of life, there is less competition and a greater desire for harmony.

23 FRIDAY
Moon Age Day 10 Moon Sign Aquarius

Issues from the past are definitely where they need to be today. In other words, it is best to let sleeping dogs lie. Apart from anything else, there is too much to get done right now and you will not wish to complicate your life too much. You are already looking ahead and planning the very end of the year.

24 SATURDAY
Moon Age Day 11 Moon Sign Pisces

Take advantage of beneficial trends coming from the direction of Mercury that are highlighting all creative pursuits. Getting things sorted is easy and will appeal to you at this time. The weekend would be good for shopping, spoiling yourself, or for short journeys leading to enjoyable encounters.

25 SUNDAY
Moon Age Day 12 Moon Sign Pisces

Communication is the key at home if you want to get on well. The more you talk to other people, the greater is the chance you will make progress. Keeping ideas to yourself is counterproductive, even when you don't think you have much to contribute. Romantically speaking, you may find new attention coming your way.

26 MONDAY
Moon Age Day 13 Moon Sign Aries

You can knock a few ideas into shape, especially in co-operation with colleagues, friends and, of course, your life partner. Natural affection on your part is a key to general progress. The more others recognise your warmth, the greater is the chance they will involve you in their schemes.

27 TUESDAY
Moon Age Day 14 Moon Sign Aries

Domestic possibilities are better than ever right now. Although this clearly isn't a time to stay at home, you will be comfortable in your own surroundings. Keep an open mind about family members who might have the odd problem, though chances are if they have need of you they will announce the fact.

28 WEDNESDAY
Moon Age Day 15 Moon Sign Taurus

Talking to some people may prove to be more trouble than it is worth today. Pick your contacts carefully and don't get too involved in gossip. What really works best at the moment is to get on with your own work quietly and expect those around you to behave in a similar manner.

29 THURSDAY
Moon Age Day 16 Moon Sign Taurus

You are looking inwards towards the deeper qualities of your nature, which really have not showed as significantly across this year as would often be the case. You need time out to contemplate your thoughts and then to plan your actions. It would be difficult to keep up a high speed today.

30 FRIDAY
Moon Age Day 17 Moon Sign Gemini

A long-standing commitment needs to be addressed as October draws to an end. Get it out of the way as quickly as you can, because what matters is leaving yourself free to do the things that come upon you quickly. Negotiating your path through a pile of red tape might not help, but you are equal enough to the task.

31 SATURDAY
Moon Age Day 18 Moon Sign Gemini

Progress today is steady, but better in the case of Crabs who work on a Saturday. Predominant trends deal with business and practical matters, whilst aspects of your personal and social life are less well accented. You should find time to talk to friends who consider themselves to be in some sort of difficulty.

November

2015

Your Month at a Glance

⊕ = Opportunities are around   ⊖ = Be on the defensive   = Life is pretty ordinary

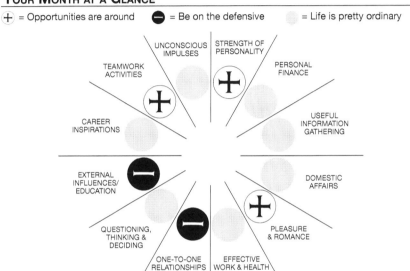

UNCONSCIOUS IMPULSES

STRENGTH OF PERSONALITY

TEAMWORK ACTIVITIES

PERSONAL FINANCE

CAREER INSPIRATIONS

USEFUL INFORMATION GATHERING

EXTERNAL INFLUENCES/ EDUCATION

DOMESTIC AFFAIRS

QUESTIONING, THINKING & DECIDING

PLEASURE & ROMANCE

ONE-TO-ONE RELATIONSHIPS

EFFECTIVE WORK & HEALTH

November Highs and Lows

Here I show you how the rhythms of the Moon will affect you this month. Like the tide, your energies and abilities will rise and fall with its pattern. When it is above the centre line, go for it, when it is below, you should be resting.

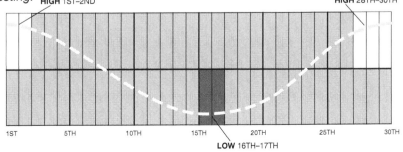

HIGH 1ST–2ND

HIGH 28TH–30TH

1ST   5TH   10TH   15TH   20TH   25TH   30TH

LOW 16TH–17TH

1 SUNDAY
Moon Age Day 19 Moon Sign Cancer

The lunar high for the start of November carries a promise of better luck and an ability to see through what might look like the fog of life clear to the heart of situations. You know what you want from life at the moment and have a fairly good idea how you are going to get it.

2 MONDAY
Moon Age Day 20 Moon Sign Cancer

There are few if any obstacles to your progress in life at the moment. The best of all worlds would find you responsive to change and anxious to follow situations through to their logical conclusions. If there are obstacles to be overcome, now is the right time to address them.

3 TUESDAY
Moon Age Day 21 Moon Sign Leo

Pressing emotional issues are dealt with quite easily, even though you might get them out of all proportion at first. You are in sight of a famous victory somewhere in your life and need only to keep going in the same direction you are following now. Friends should prove to be very supportive.

4 WEDNESDAY
Moon Age Day 22 Moon Sign Leo

Your professional ambition is now much increased, leading you to thinking about work, even if you are not actually there today. Beware of a little confusion in the family that could lead to some very funny situations, on a day during which your general sense of humour is going off the scale in any case.

5 THURSDAY
Moon Age Day 23 Moon Sign Leo

Opt for some light relief if possible. You are in a state of mind that makes it impossible for you to take yourself or anyone else very seriously. There are gains coming as a result of things you did in the past. This might cause you to look back and adopt a previous strategy again.

6 FRIDAY
Moon Age Day 24 Moon Sign Virgo

All of a sudden, the Crab becomes very competitive. This is due to the present position of the planet Mars and means that you want to reach the winning post first in almost any sort of situation. You remain essentially co-operative and believe in teamwork – just as long as you are in charge of the team!

7 SATURDAY
Moon Age Day 25 Moon Sign Virgo

Communication issues will not work out quite the way you had intended. Others can so easily get the wrong end of the stick now and this is partly because you are not explaining yourself in the way you could. Review past events if you must today, but don't let too much thinking about them get in the way of present decisions.

8 SUNDAY
Moon Age Day 26 Moon Sign Libra

You have some ingenious methods for getting ahead right now and can make the most of even little opportunities that come your way. Although you find yourself somewhat frustrated by the attitude or opinions of specific friends, you are wise enough to know there are reasons for this strange behaviour.

9 MONDAY
Moon Age Day 27 Moon Sign Libra

Clear communication is necessary if you want to enjoy a successful life early this week. Make sure others know perfectly well what you are saying, and why. On another front, you might notice that there are many personal compliments coming your way, maybe from interesting directions.

10 TUESDAY
Moon Age Day 28 Moon Sign Libra

You can probably look forward to a little ego boost in social encounters, because more compliments are likely to be coming your way. Under present circumstances this situation is hardly likely to turn your head, but it is good to know that people notice you and want to be pleasant.

11 WEDNESDAY
Moon Age Day 29 Moon Sign Scorpio

Throw negative thinking straight into a bin and get on with living your life as positively as you can. Rules and regulations are almost certain to get on your nerves, even if you were originally responsible for instigating some of them yourself. It is really important that you find ways to enjoy today.

12 THURSDAY
Moon Age Day 0 Moon Sign Scorpio

Compromises don't come easy to you now and you will have to try that little bit harder to deal with behaviour and attitudes you don't entirely understand. What you can be sure of today is that the future looks generally brighter and that you are now socialising more than of late.

13 FRIDAY
Moon Age Day 1 Moon Sign Sagittarius

A socially favourable day and one during which you can enhance your financial wherewithal, simply by saying and doing the right things. Don't get stuck on specifics, because it is the broad cross-section of life that matters at the moment. It might have occurred to you for the first time today that Christmas is just around the corner.

14 SATURDAY
Moon Age Day 2 Moon Sign Sagittarius

Today should be very enjoyable from a social point of view, even if you can't get everything you want in a material sense. In a way, that won't matter because the most important gifts that come to you now cost nothing in monetary terms. Putting a price on love, respect and genuine affection is impossible.

15 SUNDAY
Moon Age Day 3 Moon Sign Sagittarius

Though certain invitations might come your way this Sunday, there is something that makes you a less socially inclined animal for the moment. This doesn't mean you are avoiding other people, but merely that at least part of your time is spent alone. Keep an open mind about some of your recently hatched schemes and ideas.

16 MONDAY
Moon Age Day 4 Moon Sign Capricorn

Perhaps you need to move swiftly with plans and duties today. There are things that need doing and some of them can only be done by you. However, don't confuse this fact with a sense that the world can't cope without you. A balanced view is necessary and you are just the person to take one.

17 TUESDAY
Moon Age Day 5 Moon Sign Capricorn

A fairly sluggish day is on the cards and a time when it might be difficult to get what you want from situations. To a great extent, you can blame the presence of the lunar low. What won't help is to push on against all the odds. It would be far better to take a rest and come out fighting in a couple of days.

18 WEDNESDAY
Moon Age Day 6 Moon Sign Aquarius

All of a sudden this is a high-spirited time, during which your charm and winning ways show quite clearly. You won't be able to disguise periods of enthusiasm that occur today, though there is no real reason to try. Even in situations where you think your knowledge is limited, others will seek your advice and assistance.

19 THURSDAY
Moon Age Day 7 Moon Sign Aquarius

Whatever happens at home today, you might be aware of a slightly edgy atmosphere. Counter this by doing what you can to make others speak out. If you start to feel bored or restricted, you need to ring the changes somehow. A visit to see friends might be just the tonic you need.

20 FRIDAY
Moon Age Day 8 Moon Sign Pisces

This is a period for entertaining new ideas and for getting your head around projects that require your personal touch. The need that others have of you, whilst somewhat demanding on occasions today, does at least inform you of your overall importance. Keep a sense of proportion in personal situations.

21 SATURDAY
Moon Age Day 9 Moon Sign Pisces

Ingenuity appears to be your middle name at the moment. Although there might not be all that much cash about now it doesn't appear to matter. So clever are you at thinking things out, you could make a silk purse out of a sow's ear. It might not be quite so easy to alter the negative attitudes of a friend.

22 SUNDAY
Moon Age Day 10 Moon Sign Aries

Your ego is stimulated by events that take place today. It appears that you are everyone's natural choice for person of the week. Although this will be pleasant, you will have practical matters on your mind and so might not spend as much time today preening yourself.

23 MONDAY
Moon Age Day 11 Moon Sign Aries

Though the necessities of life might appear to hamper a few of your freedoms today, in a general sense you know what you want and have a pretty good idea about how you are going to get it. Don't allow boredom to creep in at any stage and remain willing to offer sound counsel to others.

24 TUESDAY
Moon Age Day 12 Moon Sign Taurus

Specific matters are now at a decisive stage and you won't want to relinquish hold over certain elements of your life. Actually, a relaxed attitude would work far better, together with a certainty that you have things well under control. The hardest thing today is conforming to the expectations of others.

25 WEDNESDAY
Moon Age Day 13 Moon Sign Taurus

Not everyone is going to have your level of enthusiasm today. It might be suggested that getting a few people going is like pushing water uphill. Maybe you shouldn't try. Stick to those who are naturally on the same wavelength as you are; otherwise the day could be fraught with minor problems.

26 THURSDAY
Moon Age Day 14 Moon Sign Gemini

Out there in the practical world, you are now achieving a number of your objectives. Not everyone will share your unique point of view, but that doesn't matter. On the contrary, even heated discussions can be grist to the mill, and the people who matter the most will not deny you your opinion.

27 FRIDAY
Moon Age Day 15 Moon Sign Gemini

Peace and quiet is what appeals to you most right now, particularly at home. You probably won't be anxious to change too much today, at a time when the position of the Moon inclines you to contemplation. However, you still carry an internal desire to find fun and excitement. Tomorrow is soon enough.

28 SATURDAY
Moon Age Day 16 Moon Sign Cancer

The green light is on and you are feeling positive and dynamic. Not everyone is in the same state of mind as you, which could mean leaving some people to catch up later. Quick on the uptake and certainly anxious to make the most of romantic possibilities, the world is your oyster around now.

29 SUNDAY
Moon Age Day 17 Moon Sign Cancer

At work, it now appears that everything is moving very smoothly indeed. Of course, if you are not committed to working on a Sunday, these trends are not able to gain ground. It is clear that from a social point of view you will still be happiest mixing with family members and maybe close friends.

30 MONDAY
Moon Age Day 18 Moon Sign Cancer

There appears to be plenty of potential for good times in a number of ways today. For those of you who have put romance on the back burner of late, there is now a greater chance of personal attention coming your way. Financial matters should be easier to resolve and relatives may prove especially helpful.

December
2015

YOUR MONTH AT A GLANCE

+ = Opportunities are around   — = Be on the defensive   = Life is pretty ordinary

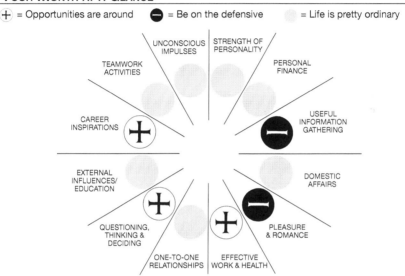

DECEMBER HIGHS AND LOWS

Here I show you how the rhythms of the Moon will affect you this month. Like the tide, your energies and abilities will rise and fall with its pattern. When it is above the centre line, go for it, when it is below, you should be resting.

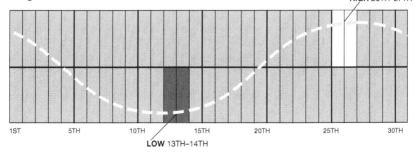

HIGH 26TH–27TH

LOW 13TH–14TH

1 TUESDAY
Moon Age Day 19 Moon Sign Leo

The main thing today is to keep on top of organisational issues. You won't be very pleased with yourself if situations become confused or if you are not keeping up with the expectations other have of you. In a more general sense, you ought to be feeling quite positive about life.

2 WEDNESDAY
Moon Age Day 20 Moon Sign Leo

The spirit of teamwork is stronger in you today and your ability to get on well with the world at large more noticeable. Take advantage of planetary trends highlighting curiosity and give in to your fascination with the way things work. Some experimentation is called for, if only to satisfy your inquisitive nature.

3 THURSDAY
Moon Age Day 21 Moon Sign Virgo

Teamwork issues remain rewarding and it looks as though you are becoming the life and soul of the party again. Active and inspirational, you respond very well to changing circumstances and will now be more willing actually to create a degree of uncertainty and even risk into your life.

4 FRIDAY
Moon Age Day 22 Moon Sign Virgo

Although friends could have a confused attitude towards specific situations, your own mind is crystal clear and you have little or no difficulty in organising yourself and others. The social whirl of Christmas might have started for you already, which could be no bad thing when you are feeling so positive.

5 SATURDAY
Moon Age Day 23 Moon Sign Libra

Gathering together all the relevant information you need should be child's play now. You are particularly well organised at the moment, which could encourage others to turn to you when they need sorting out. It might be necessary to fend off one or two social invitations, if only because you can't do everything.

6 SUNDAY
Moon Age Day 24 Moon Sign Libra

Certain sacrifices have to be made today if you want to get the very best out of any relationship. Although there are things you want to do, now may not be the right time to address them. You are spreading yourself quite thinly already and could probably do with offloading unnecessary tasks or information.

7 MONDAY   *Moon Age Day 25 Moon Sign Libra*

The time is right to have a chat with your partner, particularly on a deep and personal level. Take advantage of positive trends favouring your sensitive and caring attitude. An issue from the past could help you to solve a slight difficulty that exists at present.

8 TUESDAY   *Moon Age Day 26 Moon Sign Scorpio*

There are great rewards to be had from even the most mundane situations, though you will have to look at matters carefully and use a good deal of intuition to get the best from any situation. It might just be that you feel you cannot break through the carefully created shell of a colleague or friend.

9 WEDNESDAY   *Moon Age Day 27 Moon Sign Scorpio*

Last-minute arrangements might well be keeping you on the hop, but the sort of activities in which you are involved supply their own momentum. You won't believe everything you hear at present and will be determined to follow your own advice, especially in situations that involve finance.

10 THURSDAY   *Moon Age Day 28 Moon Sign Sagittarius*

Although you might feel that your influence over everyday matters is slightly limited, you would probably be wrong. Be willing to take a few chances and to push the bounds of credibility when it comes to your own ideas. Romance could loom large in your thinking and compliments are not hard to come by.

11 FRIDAY   *Moon Age Day 0 Moon Sign Sagittarius*

Career developments should now be going your way, though on a day that has much to recommend it in terms of sociability and general happenings, work could be the last thing on your mind. Even casual conversations with others can lead you to far-reaching conclusions.

12 SATURDAY   *Moon Age Day 1 Moon Sign Sagittarius*

When it comes to long-term plans and ambitions, you certainly have your thinking head on right now. A positive response to the ideas of others is more than likely and you mix freely with all sorts of people. It might be within your power to heal a rift that has been in existence for some time.

13 SUNDAY
Moon Age Day 2 Moon Sign Capricorn

Be prepared to deal with some limitations today. The lunar low this month comes at a time when you are not exactly feeling dynamic in any case. Try to remain positive in your attitude, but avoid making too many decisions for the next couple of days.

14 MONDAY
Moon Age Day 3 Moon Sign Capricorn

It can take a good deal longer to get where you want to be today, even in a practical, travel sense. For this reason, all arrangements need to be double-checked. Don't be too quick to make an important decision at work, or one that could have definite implications further down the line.

15 TUESDAY
Moon Age Day 4 Moon Sign Aquarius

Maybe your ego is running just a little too strongly today. Remember your natural humility, which is what sets Cancer subjects apart from the crowd. Your quiet but attractive nature is part of the reason others love you so much. Be willing to offer sound advice to almost anyone who asks.

16 WEDNESDAY
Moon Age Day 5 Moon Sign Aquarius

This is a great time for the simpler pleasures of life and, to a certain extent, for merely pleasing yourself. Some of the responsibilities of life are removed, or at least reduced. All in all, you can relax in the bosom of your family or decide on a social meeting with friends, though possibly nothing hectic.

17 THURSDAY
Moon Age Day 6 Moon Sign Pisces

On a practical footing, it is true that some things can go wrong today, though if you keep your eye on the ball this fact is not likely to worry you too much. Stand by for what could be a very humorous day, particularly if you see the funny side of things and are willing to laugh at yourself a little.

18 FRIDAY
Moon Age Day 7 Moon Sign Pisces

Once again, the day is good for all aspects of love and romance. It isn't entirely certain that you will be in a particular practical frame of mind or that your decisions in this sphere are entirely rational. What you will do now is to laugh a great deal, which is good for you and those around you.

19 SATURDAY
Moon Age Day 8 Moon Sign Aries

There are certainly some challenges to be faced today, but it is unlikely that these would bother you in any way. There is a chance for a shopping trip or for spending a few quiet hours wrapping up the last of those presents. If you aren't as organised as usual this year, don't worry too much.

20 SUNDAY
Moon Age Day 9 Moon Sign Aries

Getting your own way with other people is hardly difficult at present. You shine like a star on the social stage and will be all smiles today. It is because you are such a joy to have around that so much attention comes your way. This is a time of year when the sign of Cancer usually shows its most entertaining face.

21 MONDAY
Moon Age Day 10 Moon Sign Aries

There is variety about, even if you have to look harder for it now than you might have expected. Don't restrict yourself to thinking or even worrying about one single matter. In reality, it would be better to put any anxiety on ice. When you look at problems again they may well have ceased to have any importance at all.

22 TUESDAY
Moon Age Day 11 Moon Sign Taurus

Taking yourself for granted might be the line of least resistance today, but how many admirers is that going to get you? If you know in your heart that you have done something well, it would be sensible to own up to the fact. You don't have to be arrogant to get on well today, simply truthful.

23 WEDNESDAY
Moon Age Day 12 Moon Sign Taurus

A continuing boost to relationships means that you can expect much in the way of rewards. This is the area of life that serves you best and the one on which you are likely to concentrate at present. Your diplomatic skills are good and will come in handy at some stage later in the day.

24 THURSDAY
Moon Age Day 13 Moon Sign Gemini

It is just possible that Christmas Eve might lead to a few false promises by people who mean well but cannot follow through. In the main, you should be happy enough, if you are not dashing around from pillar to post. If you are in a shopping centre or even out in the street, take some time to join in with the fun.

25 FRIDAY
Moon Age Day 14 Moon Sign Gemini

Look out for an extremely interesting and varied sort of Christmas Day. It could be that not everyone in your family and friendship circle is having quite as good a time as you are and this could lead to extra effort on your part. The most enjoyable associations today come from close, personal attachments.

26 SATURDAY
Moon Age Day 15 Moon Sign Cancer

This is a high point in the month during which you are turning your attention towards plans you have been wishing to put into action for some time. Your general level of energy is high and good luck attends many of your efforts. Act now for maximum benefit in the days and weeks to come.

27 SUNDAY
Moon Age Day 16 Moon Sign Cancer

Get an early start with all-important issues and maybe even think about travelling somewhere today. The romantic trends look especially good and might lead to some promises being made that are long overdue. If congratulations are in order somewhere in the family, be first to offer them.

28 MONDAY
Moon Age Day 17 Moon Sign Leo

Home life and practical matters should prove to be quite enjoyable today and you have plenty of energy when it matters the most. Fair in your dealings with others, you may be asked to mediate between two friends. There is no reason to refuse, unless you sense an embarrassing outcome.

29 TUESDAY
Moon Age Day 18 Moon Sign Leo

It appears that the greatest joy of today comes from your love life, which is likely to be as enjoyable as you would wish. Something you have done for someone else in the past is now paid back with dividends. Expecting the best of others is worthwhile at present since they are unlikely to let you down.

30 WEDNESDAY
Moon Age Day 19 Moon Sign Virgo

Don't allow loved ones to feel neglected. This is a day during which you will have to offer a great deal of understanding. In terms of actually doing anything to help, you may feel rather incapable. What matters is that you are on hand when your support is needed in a psychological sense.

31 THURSDAY

Encounters with others may inspire some new ideas today. Get out and about as much as possible and certainly aim to have a really good time tonight. As for New Year resolutions, it might be best to leave them on the shelf for the moment. You will think more clearly about them once January actually arrives.

How to Calculate Your Rising Sign

Most astrologers agree that, next to the Sun Sign, the most important influence on any person is the Rising Sign at the time of their birth. The Rising Sign represents the astrological sign that was rising over the eastern horizon when each and every one of us came into the world. It is sometimes also called the Ascendant.

Let us suppose, for example, that you were born with the Sun in the zodiac sign of Libra. This would bestow certain characteristics on you that are likely to be shared by all other Librans. However, a Libran with Aries Rising would show a very different attitude towards life, and of course relationships, than a Libran with Pisces Rising.

For these reasons, this book shows how your zodiac Rising Sign has a bearing on all the possible positions of the Sun at birth. Simply look through the Aries table opposite.

As long as you know your approximate time of birth the graph will show you how to discover your Rising Sign.

Look across the top of the graph of your zodiac sign to find your date of birth, and down the side for your birth time (I have used Greenwich Mean Time). Where they cross is your Rising Sign. Don't forget to subtract an hour (or two) if appropriate for Summer Time.

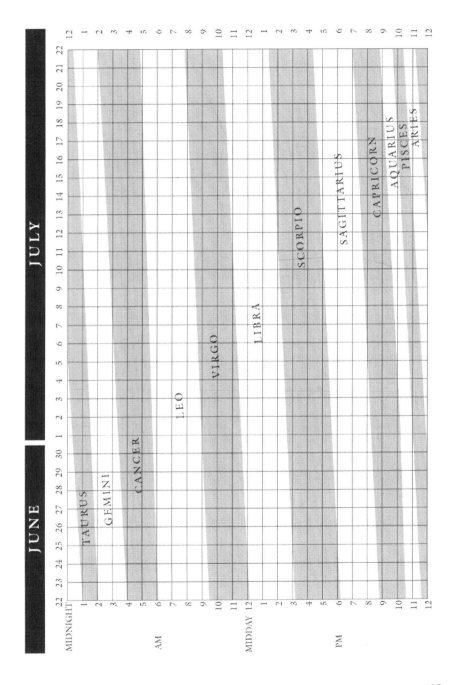

THE ZODIAC, PLANETS AND CORRESPONDENCES

The Earth revolves around the Sun once every calendar year, so when viewed from Earth the Sun appears in a different part of the sky as the year progresses. In astrology, these parts of the sky are divided into the signs of the zodiac and this means that the signs are organised in a circle. The circle begins with Aries and ends with Pisces.

Taking the zodiac sign as a starting point, astrologers then work with all the positions of planets, stars and many other factors to calculate horoscopes and birth charts and tell us what the stars have in store for us.

The table below shows the planets and Elements for each of the signs of the zodiac. Each sign belongs to one of the four Elements: Fire, Air, Earth or Water. Fire signs are creative and enthusiastic; Air signs are mentally active and thoughtful; Earth signs are constructive and practical; Water signs are emotional and have strong feelings.

It also shows the metals and gemstones associated with, or corresponding with, each sign. The correspondence is made when a metal or stone possesses properties that are held in common with a particular sign of the zodiac.

Finally, the table shows the opposite of each star sign – this is the opposite sign in the astrological circle.

Placed	Sign	Symbol	Element	Planet	Metal	Stone	Opposite
1	Aries	Ram	Fire	Mars	Iron	Bloodstone	Libra
2	Taurus	Bull	Earth	Venus	Copper	Sapphire	Scorpio
3	Gemini	Twins	Air	Mercury	Mercury	Tiger's Eye	Sagittarius
4	Cancer	Crab	Water	Moon	Silver	Pearl	Capricorn
5	Leo	Lion	Fire	Sun	Gold	Ruby	Aquarius
6	Virgo	Maiden	Earth	Mercury	Mercury	Sardonyx	Pisces
7	Libra	Scales	Air	Venus	Copper	Sapphire	Aries
8	Scorpio	Scorpion	Water	Pluto	Plutonium	Jasper	Taurus
9	Sagittarius	Archer	Fire	Jupiter	Tin	Topaz	Gemini
10	Capricorn	Goat	Earth	Saturn	Lead	Black Onyx	Cancer
11	Aquarius	Waterbearer	Air	Uranus	Uranium	Amethyst	Leo
12	Pisces	Fishes	Water	Neptune	Tin	Moonstone	Virgo